La Guerre Est Finie

Also by Jorge Semprun:

The Long Voyage (Winner of the 1963 $10,000 Formentor Novel Prize)

Also by Alain Resnais:

Hiroshima Mon Amour (Text by Marguerite Duras)
Last Year at Marienbad (Text by Alain Robbe-Grillet)

La Guerre Est Finie

Text by Jorge Semprun
For the Film by Alain Resnais

Translated by Richard Seaver
Film Editor: Robert Hughes

Grove Press, Inc. New York

Library of Congress Catalog Card Number: 67-30113

Manufactured in the United States of America
First Printing

For Florence

The militant does not ask that his action justify him: he *is*, and needs no subsequent justification. But his personality encompasses his own justification, since it is constituted by the end to be attained. Thus it is relative to the action, which itself is relative to the goal. As for the action itself, it should rightly be termed an undertaking, for it is a slow, stubborn task of edification, which goes on indefinitely.

—Jean-Paul Sartre

Contents

I

To Warn Juan

BEHOBIE BRIDGE. 7:15 A.M. Sunday, April 18, 1965.

Beginning with the first shot—perhaps even a fraction of a second before the first shot appears—the Narrator's Voice can be heard.

The Voice can be heard over the shot of a car, a black Peugeot 404 which has just left Spain via the old Behobie Bridge. In the background, the sun is rising over the green hills of Elizondo.

The Voice can be heard over the shot of the faces of two men in the car. Behind the glass of the windshield, their faces are motionless. Is it the long drive throughout the night which has made their faces look gaunt? In any case, their faces are drawn and haggard.

Now that the Voice has spoken a few words, a few sentences, the picture freezes on the face of the Passenger. It is a familiar voice, as though it were the double of the car's occupant who is relating this story. As though the Narrator knew the car's occupant, around whom the story revolves, very well.

NARRATOR'S VOICE: You've gotten through. Once again you're looking at the Biriatou hill, you're feeling how it is to have made it—a slightly insipid, slightly tense feeling. You've been driving all night, your mouth is dry from the lack of sleep, from smoking. Once again you're crossing this border, in the shimmering light of early morning. Behind you, the sun is rising over the Elizondo peaks. Once again, you're going to make it through.

The faces of two men, motionless, tight-lipped, in a car which, moving slowly, emerges from the Behobie Bridge. And behind them, on the left, the sun barely grazing the peaks of the Elizondo hills.

The car's passenger turns around and looks back at the sun rising over the Spanish countryside, beyond the little Behobie Bridge. When he turns back toward the road in front of the car, a slight smile briefly flits across his face.

The Peugeot has just passed the fork in the road which turns off to the right toward Biriatou, and continues ahead toward the French customs shed some thirty or forty yards beyond. Several cars parked in front of the checkpoint are having their papers and documents checked by the customs officials.

A uniformed C.R.S. policeman * *stationed in the middle of the road to direct traffic signals for them to stop.*

The Peugeot has come to a complete stop.

After having rolled down his window, the Passenger glances at the cars parked in front of the customs shed.

He rolls the window half way back up and lights a cigarette.

The Driver stretches, to relax his arm muscles, which have grown tight during the long drive. He turns to the Passenger.

THE DRIVER: No problem: we'll make your train all right.

The Passenger does not reply. He says nothing.

He is smoking, wedged comfortably in the front seat, resigned to waiting in line. His mind wanders from this car, this forced

---

* C.R.S.: *Corps Republicain de Sécurité,* an elite French police corps.—*Translator's note.*

wait (however minimal or ridiculous it may be at the end of such a long voyage). His mind moves ahead to the things he is going to have to do.

Various images, sometimes short and lightning-like, sometimes slow and unwinding, sometimes sharp and at other times unclear, follow one after the other. Images, all of which relate to movement, to action: a train thundering silently on its way. A picture of the Passenger himself hurrying toward the exit of the Austerlitz station in Paris, deserted and ghostlike. Blocks of government-subsidized, low-income apartment buildings in one of the Paris suburbs. Elevators full of people, empty hallways through which he walks, silently, toward doors that open, faces of women who listen to him attentively. And, again, images of movement: cars, driven at top speed, racing through the night.

At the center of this whirlpool of mental images, as though they all were converging toward him or derived from him, a man's face, perceived in the brilliance of memory (and perhaps with the frozen stillness of a photograph), now seen as a whole and then at times in various of its details: his eyes, his chin, his mouth.

During this brief mental foray on the part of the Passenger, this foray into the future, the Driver's Voice is heard.

*

Since he has first said that they were sure of making the train (in fact he said "your train," stressing the possessive, perhaps in order to point up the more direct, or more vital, relationship between his companion and this train that has to be caught, perhaps to point up the fact that he, the Driver, is simply responsible for getting his companion to this train on time), since he has uttered these first words, the Driver has not stopped talking.

DRIVER'S VOICE: All night I was worried the car might break down. . . . There was no reason to, though, I had had the car checked. Some kind of crazy obsession, you know how it is. At night, in the middle of nowhere, between Burgos and Miranda, for example, with all those miles of nothing on every side . . . Because, I don't mean any offense, mind you, but service stations in your country aren't exactly what you'd call numerous. So I didn't drive as fast as I might have, I was afraid. . . . If it weren't for you, I would have gone touristing today. . . . A good meal in a seafood restaurant . . . Soft-shelled crab, with a good Ribeiro white wine . . . Or maybe roast pork at Botin's, behind the Plaza Mayor . . . And of course, this afternoon, the bullfight . . . Generally I don't have time, I don't even get a chance to do any sightseeing in the towns I go to. . . . You may not believe me, but I haven't even set foot yet in the Prado. . . .

His face, visible now, energetic and pleasant, turns toward the Passenger. Behind the wheel, he smiles and stretches.

THE DRIVER: Now I can tell you: last night, when you told me that we were going to have to leave right away, I was furious.

The Passenger's reply to him is calm.

THE PASSENGER: It was fairly obvious, you know. We generally spend the night talking, but last night you acted as though I didn't exist.

They both laugh.

THE DRIVER: I'd arranged things to be away three days. My wife was going to look after the bookstore till Tuesday. Today, the Prado. Tomorrow, Toledo and Aranjuez. Three days of vacation, actually. So, you see, last night when you read the letter I brought you and then you made me leave immediately, I was in a foul mood.

The Passenger looks at him. He smiles.

THE PASSENGER: What you're saying is, I ruined your trip.

They both laugh.

I guess you'd better lodge a complaint with the Spanish police.

On the opposite side of the road the line of cars is already fairly long. Bumper to bumper, they move forward in little spurts toward the Behobie Bridge, going into Spain.

Having nothing better to do while they wait, both men mechanically watch the line of cars.

Lots of people already at this hour.

THE DRIVER: It's Easter. They're going to spend the day in Spain.

The cars go by, on the other side of the road. Through the open window on the driver's side drift the sounds of the motors changing gears as the line of cars moves forward in little spurts.

THE DRIVER: That makes it easier for you. They hardly have time to examine the passports any more.

The Passenger shakes his head.

How did you used to do it, before?

THE PASSENGER: Before?

THE DRIVER: When the border was closed, before there were any tourists?

The Passenger looks at the line of cars.

THE PASSENGER: We used to cross over through the mountains.

He snuffs out his cigarette in the ashtray on the dashboard of the car.

Sometimes we ran into the Guardia Civil.

THE DRIVER: What happened then?

THE PASSENGER: Then we had to shoot our way through.

The Driver has a fairly pronounced accent from the Southwest of France. The Passenger has no accent at all.

The Policeman signals for them to advance.

Now they are next to the customs shed. The Passenger opens the glove compartment and takes from it the car's registration papers, both passports, and hands them to the Driver. A customs official has come over to the car, on the driver's side.

He takes the papers that are handed to him, and glances at them.

The Passenger has lighted another cigarette.

The customs official looks at the passports, at the car's documents. He moves away to glance at the license plate. Then he walks over to a Policeman who is standing a few yards away, watching the customs formalities.

Inside the car, the Driver turns to his Passenger, smiling.

THE DRIVER: With you, I'm happy to say, there's no problem.

The Passenger looks at him.

THE PASSENGER: What do you mean?

THE DRIVER: To hear you talk, no one would ever guess you're Spanish.

The Passenger watches the line of cars moving forward into his country.

THE PASSENGER: Even I forget sometimes.

They laugh, as though it were funny. As though they were part of some big joke.

THE DRIVER: Last time, I brought a buddy through the border who couldn't speak a word of French. He pretended to be half asleep. Still, if they had asked him the slightest question, we would have been screwed.

They laugh again, with the complicity born of the long drive they have taken together, of dangers shared.

With you it's a cinch.

While they have been speaking, the Policeman and the customs official have come over and stationed themselves close beside the car.

As the Driver finishes his last word, the Policeman bends down, until his head is framed in the open window of the car, on the driver's side. He glances around the inside of the car.

POLICEMAN: Gentlemen . . .

He looks at the two men, and the two men look back at him.

Please park your car beyond the shed and come with me to the police station.

With his hand he gestures to an empty parking space beyond the customs shed.

THE DRIVER: But why? I'm in a hurry.

The Policeman's face is a mask of seriousness and mystery: it is, at this moment, the very personification of power. He knows full well that he does not have to offer any explanation, that he doesn't have to justify in the slightest any orders he gives. He incarnates power, purely and simply. And yet he does his job without any undue lack of civility, or any display of vulgarity.

POLICEMAN: Police check. Drive the car up there.

The Driver is rather inclined to argue some more, but from behind him he hears the voice of the Passenger, surprisingly neutral.

THE PASSENGER: Go on, do as he says.

Then the Driver furiously rolls up his window, as if by so doing he were proving his independence and banishing from sight the image of the Policeman. He puts the car into first gear.

Flanked on one side by the Policeman and on the other by the customs official, he drives it slowly toward the area beyond the customs shed.

In spite of the closed window, and the noise of the motor which is still in first gear, the Driver lowers his voice as he speaks.

THE DRIVER: What's this all about?
THE PASSENGER: You know as much as I do.
THE DRIVER: You think it's a chance verification?

The Passenger makes a gesture indicating he has no idea.

Are you sure your papers are O.K., Carlos?

There is a certain aggressive edge discernible in this question. As though the Driver were making the Passenger responsible for whatever may happen. In a sense, he is right.

THE PASSENGER: Remember what we said. Not another word. It's got to be O.K.

The Policeman, who has been walking beside the car as it moves forward, makes a sign for them to stop. Then he comes over to the car. He is holding both passports and the car's documents in his hand.

POLICEMAN: Leave the keys in the car. Follow me.

Both men get out of the Peugeot 404.

THE DRIVER: What about the baggage?
POLICEMAN: Leave it inside. No need to bring it.

He points to the customs shed and gestures for them to head for it.

They begin walking toward it, followed by the Policeman.

*

The Passenger is slightly taller than the Driver, thinner too. But he is older: he must be a good forty, the other man roughly ten years younger.

The Passenger is dressed in a gray flannel suit, a checked sport shirt, with a button-down collar, open at the neck. He is wearing suede shoes. The general impression he makes is one of a certain elegance. Perhaps this is simply because he seems to be completely at ease.

The Driver is heavier-set. He is dressed in a more "provincial" fashion: dark suit, white shirt, and tie. He is wearing a solid pair of black shoes, which are probably cleated at the toe; in any case, his footsteps resound on the pavement, whereas his companion moves silently as he walks. He seems more embarrassed, more nervous than his companion.

Just as they reach the customs shed, another C.R.S. policeman is making another couple get out of their car, which is also a black Peugeot 404.

THE PASSENGER: You've got it in for the 404's today!

He has turned his head to speak to the Policeman following them. But the Policeman remains impassive and says nothing in reply.

*

After the sun of a while back, after the green horizon of the Elizondo hills, the flashes of silver on the water of the Bidassoa, the customs-shed office offers an impression of dusty, oppressive boredom. The place seems impregnated with an odor of old paper and stale tobacco.

An Inspector in civilian clothes is taking notes in a notebook. Spread out on the table before him are their passports and the car's documents.

He finishes writing something and raises his head.

INSPECTOR: Yes?

Before him is the car's Passenger, alone.

THE PASSENGER: That's the whole story. I bought some books and magazines from him. We struck up an acquaintance.
INSPECTOR: So, Monsieur René Sallanches, you were on vacation there?

THE PASSENGER: That's correct.
INSPECTOR: Alone?
THE PASSENGER: Yes, alone.
INSPECTOR: You live in Paris, at 4, rue de l'Estrapade?
THE PASSENGER: No, 7.
INSPECTOR: And you met Monsieur Jude in his bookshop, Monsieur Sallanches?
THE PASSENGER: That's correct.

INSPECTOR: Madame Jude . . . what's her first name again?
THE PASSENGER: Marie . . . She's charming.

The Inspector looks at him. A transparent, noncommital look. Neither friendly nor hostile. One has the impression that he is merely doing his job. Silence. Then the Inspector speaks, in a harsher tone.

INSPECTOR: Do you have a telephone in Paris, Monsieur Sallanches?
THE PASSENGER: Of course.

He snuffs out the cigarette that he has been smoking in an ashtray on the Inspector's desk. He leans forward to do this, and the Inspector cannot see his eyes. He straightens up.

A certain amount of time—a few seconds, a fraction of a minute—has gone by, for he has made all these movements slowly.

Of course: MEDICIS 33-74.

The Inspector notes the number on a piece of paper. He gets up and walks to the door. When he opens that door, another office appears, as forlorn as the first. The Inspector stands on the threshold of the open door.

INSPECTOR: Ledoux! Get me this number right away!

Someone in the second office has moved, and he comes over to the door—doubtless another inspector.

The two men exchange a few words, in low tones, and the second inspector takes the piece of paper on which the telephone number is marked.

The door closes again.

When the first Inspector comes back toward him, the face of the Passenger is masklike, motionless, distracted.

Suddenly a smile unfreezes the mask.

THE PASSENGER: At this time of morning you're going to wake Nadine.

INSPECTOR: Nadine?

*

Through the open door between the two offices, the Passenger and the inspector who was called Ledoux enter the latter's office.

The Driver is there. He watches the Passenger arrive, a shadow of anxiety on his face.

A telephone is standing on the table, the receiver is off the hook.

We hear the voice of the Inspector who interrogated the Passenger.

INSPECTOR'S VOICE: I told her that you hadn't been in an accident, but she wants to speak to you. She's worried.

The Passenger has picked up the receiver. Ledoux, standing beside him, observes him, as does the Driver.

THE PASSENGER: Nadine?

He sees the Inspector observing him carefully.

NADINE'S VOICE: What's happened? Did you run over another old lady?

THE PASSENGER: Don't be silly! Everything's all right.

He sees an ashtray filled with butts.

NADINE'S VOICE: Why did that inspector telephone?
THE PASSENGER: A simple formality.

He sees the dusty file folders.

NADINE'S VOICE: Can't he mind his own business?
THE PASSENGER: These things happen, you know.

He sees Inspector Ledoux's eyes, still watchful.

Will you be home tonight?
NADINE'S VOICE: Yes, I'll wait for you.

There is a musty odor in the office, banal objects of a ridiculous reality.

THE PASSENGER: So I'll see you tonight at the house. Good-by.

Again his eyes meet Inspector Ledoux's.

'Bye, darling.

He hangs up the phone. He is pensive. Inspector Ledoux says nothing.

THE ROAD BETWEEN BEHOBIE AND HENDAYE. 8:15 A.M.

Watched by a C.R.S. policeman until they drive away, the two travelers are getting settled back in the 404.

The car moves out onto the road leading to Hendaye.

The Passenger opens the glove compartment and looks at the objects inside.

The Passenger has been referred to as Carlos. That may be an assumed name, but for the sake of simplicity we'll call him Carlos. As for the Driver, there is no doubt about his name: it was the Inspector who referred to him as Monsieur Jude, from his papers. Monsieur Jude, a bookseller in Hendaye.

CARLOS: They searched the car.

Jude shrugs his shoulders, furiously.

JUDE: What did you expect?

This incident seems to have upset him considerably.

CARLOS: So, what did you tell him?

JUDE: I told him you were down here on vacation. That you came into my shop to buy some books and magazines. We struck up an acquaintance. That we had decided, for no special reason, that I would come down and pick you up in Spain. Then when I said that, he asked me: "In Madrid?" "Yes," I said, "what's so special about that?" And he said: "That's quite a drive in twenty-four hours. Five hundred kilometers each way. It doesn't give you much time for sightseeing." That riled me. So I merely said to him: "I like to drive. It relaxes me."

There is a moment of strained silence.

THE PASSENGER: Is the first train I can catch now the Sud-Express?

JUDE: Yes. It leaves at 9:55. First class only.

THE PASSENGER: Nine fifty-five? Then I have time to see Antoine!

JUDE: Don't you want me to give him the message for you, the way we agreed?

THE PASSENGER: What for, since I have the time.

Jude doesn't reply immediately; he is thinking.

JUDE: Listen, I'd prefer we weren't seen arriving together at Antoine's. Here's what we'll do. I'll drop you off at the house, and I'll go tell Antoine you're here. I'll tell him to meet you at the station, fifteen minutes before train time. Better play it safe.

AT THE JUDE HOME, HENDAYE. 8:35 A.M.

The sound of an electric razor buzzing.

The Passenger is finishing shaving in the Jude bathroom.

He puts his electric razor back in a toilet kit, which he repacks in his handbag.

From his handbag he takes a clean shirt and a tie. He puts the tie next to the shirt to see if the colors go together. He is satisfied they do.

During this time, we hear the Passenger's Voice. Not an interior voice monologuing without inflection, but a precise voice, as though he were speaking to someone, explaining something to him. And yet his lips are closed.

CARLOS' VOICE: He asked me if I had a telephone. I replied automatically. But I had a blank. Nothing: a total blank. I had forgotten René Sallanches' phone number. "That does it," I thought, "that does it. We're going to be caught because of this tiny detail." In any case, even if I managed to remember the phone number, it was impossible to predict what the party on the other end was going to answer. If the Inspector had reached René Sallanches himself . . .

Now they are in a room in the Jude's apartment.

The Passenger is speaking to Monsieur and Madame Jude. He is cleanly shaven and has put on a slightly faded blue shirt, with a striped wool tie. He is seated at a table on which are some cups and a coffee pot. Across from him, Madame Jude, young and rather pretty. Jude is standing behind his wife's chair, showing a one-day stubble of beard.

There is no break or interruption in the sound track.

THE PASSENGER: . . . our goose would have been cooked.

MADAME JUDE: If I understand correctly, the passport is false, but the telephone number correct?

The Passenger and Madame Jude exchange glances.

In her secret thoughts and feelings, Madame Jude is being unjust at present. For her husband has run the same risks as his Passenger, and yet it's he she is looking at, with a mixture of interest and admiration discernible in her eyes.

THE PASSENGER: Everything is true. René Sallanches, his passport, his daughter, his telephone. . . . I'm the only thing false in the whole story.

All three of them laugh, a bit stupidly, or automatically, as happens in such cases.

MADAME JUDE: In short, only the photo is changed.

The Passenger nods.

CARLOS: That's one way of putting it.

Then Jude speaks, in the manner of someone who knows the inner workings of such matters. Perhaps, vaguely or subconsciously, he wants to draw his wife's attention to himself.

He bends over his wife.

JUDE: You see, Marie, it's not any more complicated than that.

But she looks as though she finds it more complicated than that. She again addresses her words to the Passenger.

MADAME JUDE: O.K., so you know all there is to know about the Sallanches family: your answers are fine. But the Sallanches, on the other hand, don't know anything about you, I mean about the person who uses the passport. And yet on the telephone they didn't betray you.

CARLOS: No, they didn't.

He leans forward and stirs his coffee. Then he raises his head and looks at Madame Jude. He looks squarely at her, and beneath his gaze her eyes widen.

CARLOS: It's my lucky star. Without it, I would long ago have been dead, or in prison.

Perhaps he shouldn't have said that. Perhaps saying that was a pretentious cliché, alluding to the dangers he runs in the life he leads. Perhaps it was because he senses Madame Jude's interest that he is led to make himself seem interesting.

He laughs, to try and erase his previous sentence.

I have no idea. Anyway, Nadine will explain it to me.

Madame Jude looks at him quizzically.

She's Sallanches' daughter. She's the one who answered the phone.

Jude interrupts.

JUDE: Do you know her?

CARLOS: I don't know anyone. I know everything I have to know about them, but I don't know anyone.

He doesn't know anyone, but he knows that Nadine is twenty, that this year she began her first, preparatory year of university studies toward a degree in literature.

*

For a brief moment he leaves the Jude apartment in Hendaye, leaves the tritely reassuring objects: some cups, a coffeepot, a television set.

In his imagination—his memory?—there pass the silhouettes, the faces, of young girls in the Latin Quarter. Rapid shots, in which the faces and bodies of the girls are sometimes unclear, but the places themselves very clear: a bookshop where, with serious mein, they are choosing books; a café where they sit and talk, laughingly. There are times, on the contrary, when the places are unclear and the faces and bodies of the girls are very sharply seen.

All these young girls' bodies have something in common:

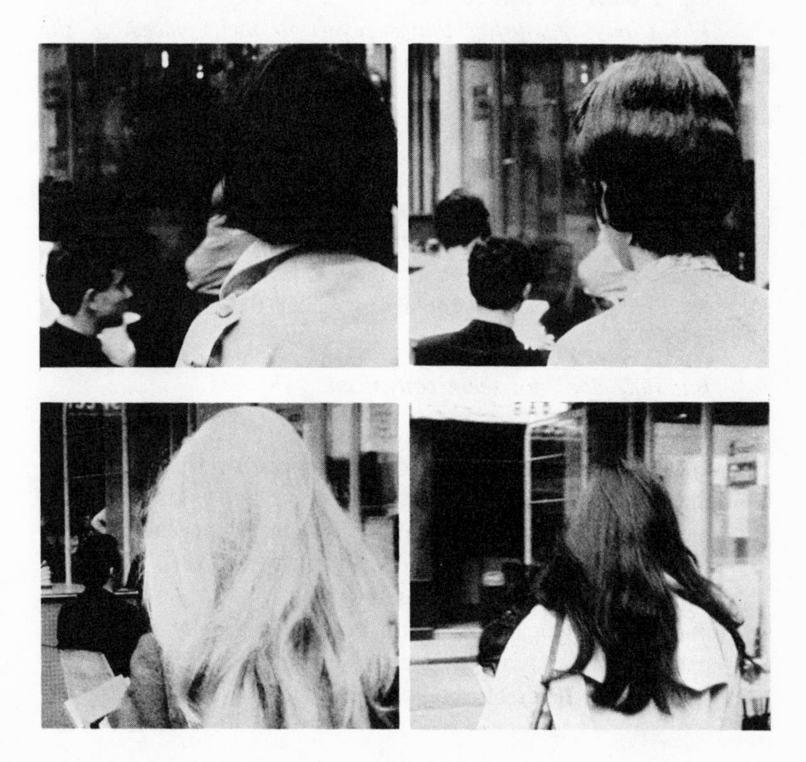

they are slim and healthy. All their faces also have something in common: a certain gravity, an analogous demanding look about them.

As he is trying to picture Nadine, Madame Jude's Voice is heard. But perhaps he doesn't hear it.

MADAME JUDE'S VOICE: I find it strange that you should speak of a lucky star. I've always thought that, I mean that there are people with lucky stars.

But Jude breaks in, bringing her back to reality, interrupting her dream.

*

JUDE: You mean to say you really think they stopped us by chance?

The Passenger turns to him.

The tritely reassuring things revert to their places, in the Jude apartment in Hendaye, on this spring day.

CARLOS: Of course I do.

JUDE: What makes you think so?

CARLOS: Didn't you see? They stopped another 404 behind us. Also black.

JUDE: Are you sure? I didn't notice.

CARLOS: They must have received some word about a suspicious car. They searched them all, those of the same make and color.

But Jude does not seem convinced.

JUDE: Why suspicious?

CARLOS: Listen, smuggling is still going on. I've had it happen that they would search our car looking for gold, for example, and they find propaganda pamphlets concealed in the car's frame.

MADAME JUDE: What happens then?

CARLOS: That depends. If it's on the French side of the border, a short prison term, a fine, or house arrest. Nothing very serious. . . . If it's on the Spanish side . . .

Madame Jude is still motionless, looking at this Spaniard her husband has driven.

Again her husband leans down to her.

JUDE: It's time to open the shop.

Yes, it's time to open the shop. She moves. Everyone moves. Madame Jude goes over to the Passenger, who has gotten to his feet.

She looks at him.

Jude and his Passenger are alone, seated near the table.

Jude rubs his dark, unshaven chin.

JUDE: You know what? I'm going to bed.

The Passenger looks at his watch.

Antoine must already be at the station.

Jude gets up. The Passenger follows suit. There is a silence. As though each of them had already taken leave of the other, gone his own way.

And what if this other guy's already crossed the border?

The Passenger makes a brusque gesture, as though he wanted to eliminate that thought, that image.

CARLOS: I tell you, it's impossible.

He shakes his head.

JUDE: Do I know him?

The Spaniard looks at Jude, and an image appears, in a sudden, searing light, in his brain: the face of the man which had already haunted him in the car, before the incident at the customs shed at Behobie.

There's still something that bothers me about that whole thing.

The Passenger makes another gesture, as if to say, "Stop worrying."

How did they know that I went to Madrid?

CARLOS: But that's the whole point, they couldn't know. The Inspector simply made a stab in the dark. He just happened to hit it right.

Jude looks at him thoughtfully.

JUDE: With all those arrests taking place in Madrid, are you sure they didn't spot you as well?

The Spaniard gives a short laugh.

CARLOS: If I were spotted, do you think the Spanish police would have let me get away?

Jude shakes his head. Obviously, that argument is convincing. But there is still a trace of anxiety on his face.

They are at the door. Jude puts his arm around the Spaniard's shoulder.

JUDE: Good luck, Carlos.

They are close together.

The Spaniard turns toward the Hendaye bookseller, and smiles.

AT THE HENDAYE STATION. In the hubbub of Sunday. 9:35 A.M.

The movement and confusion of a border station unfolds before the eyes of the Passenger as he walks toward the precise spot where he is to meet Antoine.

Suddenly, in the commotion of voices, the dominant language is Spanish. Not that one can really hear it, or understand the words that are spoken or shouted, but the sonority and rhythm of these voices are clearly Spanish.

Entire families are grouped around piles of baggage. Groups of men who are on their way to work abroad are standing in silent clusters. The strident voices of mothers call out to children who have wandered off.

The Passenger walks through this crowd, this chaos structured around the compact masses of families and groups, this welter of familiar voices.

Among all these faces he is looking for one face, one silhouette among all these silhouettes. The face, the silhouette of Antoine, which he projects onto the screen of his mind, comparing it to the faces and outlines of the crowd.

And then this face and outline of Antoine leave the realm of imagination and take form: Antoine is before him.

ANTOINE: Salud, compadrito!

He has spoken to him in Spanish, with a noticeable French accent, utilizing the term "compadrito," which is an Argentinean expression he must have heard used in some Tango.

CARLOS: Hello!

They meet, but they do not stop, in order to talk. They are going to keep on walking through the crowd of Sunday travelers, in the midst of the Sunday Spanish voices.

Juan? Has Juan arrived?

He has pronounced the name "Juan" in Spanish, the rest of the phrase in his adopted tongue.

ANTOINE: Juan? No, no news of Juan.

CARLOS: They haven't told you he's coming?

ANTOINE: You know, there are times when I don't know who's coming. They ask me to get a car ready, that's all.

CARLOS: Who's crossed over during the past few days?

ANTOINE: Yesterday there were two cars, for Andalusia. Guys who offered to spend their vacations working for us. This morning, a car for Bilbao, the same one that goes every two weeks. And I have a car ready, Paris sent me word to prepare it, but I don't know for whom.

CARLOS: For how many days?

ANTOINE: If you want my opinion, he's going across the border via Perpignan.

The idea seems to frighten the Passenger.

*

His mental images unfold, headlong images impinging one upon the other, as though something had gone wrong in his intimate projection of the possible future.

Juan is in a car, motionless. He is behind the wheel, he tries to start the car but nothing happens, as in those dreams when one can no longer manage to take a step. A tight knot of men with tense-looking but indistinct faces walk toward the car, which won't start. The group surrounds the car and keeps it from going.

CARLOS: What makes you think so?

ANTOINE: He's made several crossings recently at this border point.

CARLOS: Perpignan?

This possibility takes him unawares.

*

He sees himself running down the station platform beside a train. On the outside of one of the cars a sign reads:

BORDEAUX-TARBES-PERPIGNAN

The train starts to move. He runs alongside it.

*

CARLOS: You don't know who's in charge of the Perpignan crossing?

Antoine shakes his head.

ANTOINE: I have no idea. It's not my sector. Anyhow, what could you accomplish by going to Perpignan?

He looks at the Passenger.
He looks at him again, more attentively.

Can you tell me what the story is with Juan?

CARLOS: Yesterday, the bookseller brought me a letter informing me of his arrival in Madrid.

They have crossed through the main lobby of the station. They stop. The crowd moves around them. Till now, they have been moving through a stationary crowd. Now it is the crowd that moves around them.

There have been some arrests. He mustn't go back.

ANTOINE: Arrests? There hasn't been a word in the papers.

They are motionless for a moment, and silent.

CARLOS: In any case, if Juan shows up here, don't let him cross the border. Tell him to wait here for further instructions.

ANTOINE: All right. But I think he's going to cross the border via Perpignan.

Carlos is alone. He is about to go through the gate leading

to the station platform. A sign reads: PASSENGERS FOR PARIS. *He looks at the sign. He retraces his steps. The Man at the information counter raises his head and looks at him.*

MAN: Perpignan? Just one moment, please.

He has the sonorous accent of Southwest France. He begins to flip through the pages of the timetable. He stops at one page, and as his finger moves down a column of figures he talks to the Passenger. He tells him what trains he must take to get to Perpignan.

MAN: Now then! You take the 3:34 P.M. train from Bayonne to Toulouse, which puts you in Toulouse at 8:34. You have a connection for Narbonne at 9:13, and at 11:01 a train from Narbonne to Perpignan. Which puts you in Perpignan at 11:55 P.M. Not exactly the fastest service in the world!

CARLOS: No, not exactly.

The Passenger, his handbag in his hand, hurries along the station platform reserved for the Sud-Express. Signs very clearly visible on the sides of the car:

SUD-EXPRESS, IRUN-BORDEAUX-PARIS.

NARRATOR'S VOICE: Juan hasn't yet crossed over, but maybe he was sent via Perpignan. You don't know, there's nothing you can do all alone. Antoine is right, you don't even know the person in Perpignan in charge of the crossings. You have to go back to Paris. Probably Juan hasn't left yet, you'll find him at home. It's imperative you see the men today, to explain to them what's going on in Madrid. No one must leave for Madrid, especially Juan. It's like putting his head in a noose.

IN THE SUD-EXPRESS. Sunday, starting at 10:30 A.M.

Earlier there had been the mental image of a train, racing along in the dizzying silence of its speed, and at present there is the countryside of Les Landes, the real countryside of Les Landes, sliding giddily beyond the window of the compartment.

At first there is only this countryside of Les Landes, sliding beneath his gaze in total silence, and yet there is also the prolonged roll and pitch of a train racing at top speed.

Then he turns his gaze to the inside of the compartment, and the continuous, repetitive murmur of the electric-driven express train is heard.

He is seated in the corner of the compartment next to the corridor, his back to the direction the train is going. Diagonally across from him is a woman, still young, her blond hair swept back by a headband, silkily dressed in cashmere.

Across from the blond young woman, whose skin is tanned from having the time to expose it to the sun and fresh air, next to the window, with his back to the direction the train is going, is a priest, whose distinguished-looking, ascetic face and silver-haired temples are seen in profile.

Seated beside this still young, still beautiful (or is hers a recent beauty, one of those women whose beauty is late-flowering?) there is a balding old man, wearing a decoration in his buttonhole. There is something stiff, something military about him.

On the same seat with the still young woman and the old man, opposite Carlos, there is a man about thirty who is beginning to put on weight. In his lightweight wool suit, he looks like a technocrat.

The old man is reading Le Figaro, *the priest is reading a book by Theilhard de Chardin,* Le Milieu Divin, *the thirty-*

year-old man is reading the magazine Planète, *and the still young woman is reading a novel by Alba de Céspèdes.*

He is not reading anything. He has just looked to see what the others are reading, but he is not reading anything.

He is seated in his corner by the corridor, and on either side of the train he sees the countryside of Les Landes flashing by.

A rustle of newspaper pages being turned; a short cough: these are the only sounds we hear. Except for the murmur, sometimes sharper, sometimes more muffled, of the express train sliding through the countryside.

The only thing one can do is daydream. He settles back in his corner and lets his mind wander.

*

The same kind of mental images which had surged through his mind this morning, before they had been stopped at the frontier.

But now, since these images do not intrude on his mind, as it were, but are chosen by him, they are more orderly, more structured, more logical, and in a more comprehensible chronology. In fact, what he is projecting on the screen of his mind are the possible scenes of his arrival in Paris.

First, the arrival at the Austerlitz station. Perfectly realistic mental images: an actual train arriving, a real Austerlitz station. Into this seeming reality of mental images, projected toward a future both unpredictable and indeterminate—one that he has already lived through and experienced (he has frequently arrived at the Austerlitz station), two elements introduce an explosive charge of unreality: the complete silence of that universe into which he is projecting himself, and the rhythm, only scarcely but nevertheless noticeably slower, of the various movements to and fro in the station.

Second, a fairly long search for someone through the hallways and courtyards, the stairways of one of the low-income apartment buildings in the Paris suburbs. Some doors remain closed to his rings; others open, but only to reveal the expressionless, impassive faces of women he doesn't know. Here, added to the unreality of the silence and the untoward slowness, is added another visual element which further detracts from the veracity of the images: day, night, dawn, dusk are superimposed one upon the other during this none the less methodical search, in keeping with a logical chronological order.

Third, a meeting, at long last, with someone (a very dark, desiccated, thin man, who is very short, someone he obviously must know, for the man himself as well as his gestures are very clearly seen) who answers him, reacts to him, who listens.

Finally, together with this man, a whole new series of efforts made, of visits to various outlying sections of Paris and to lower-class quarters, this time the rhythm of the images being rapid rather than slow, accelerated, impinging upon one another. And, at the end of this search, again the image of this same man's face which was already at the center of the welter of mental images seen earlier this morning: the image of Juan, who must be stopped from leaving, so that he will not fall into the hands of the Spanish police.

The encounter with Juan, spirited and animated, imagined from various viewpoints, depending on the various personal relationships, always takes place in the same spot, which in fact does not seem suited to a meeting of this kind; and this spot, in any case, pre-empts all the other places, the other sites in Paris where the search for Juan—who has at last been found —has hitherto unfolded: a large, quiet room, with tall windows from another era, tastefully furnished, overlooking the quays of the Seine, with, in the background, the familiar view of the Left Bank.

During this time, however, perceptive contact with the real world of the train, of the compartment, has not been completely lost. As a counterpoint to the interior silence of all these images, there were the sounds of the train, which at times were perceptible, the muffled voices of people passing in the corridor, and an occasional word or two exchanged in the compartment itself. Interspersed in this succession of mental images, and occasionally breaking in upon it, were shots of the compartment, its occupants, and the countryside flying past.

He shakes himself out of his daydream. He feels like smoking. He looks around him. None of the other passengers is smoking. And yet it's a compartment where smoking is permitted. He sees the sign written in reverse on the glass of the compartment door. There is an ashtray within arm's length.

He lights a cigarette.

At the sound of the match striking, four faces are raised from behind their books, newspapers, and magazines, and four pairs of eyes are riveted upon him.

He pays no attention to the gazes of the men, including that of the priest. But he accepts the woman's, he meets her gaze. She lowers her eyes back on her book. He keeps on staring at her. She raises her eyes, with an irritated flutter of her eyelids. He keeps up the game once or twice more. Then he gets up and goes out into the corridor.

He smokes, leaning on the guardrail along the window, now letting the vision of the countryside that is flying past fill his gaze.

There is nothing but the countryside, the boredom of the voyage.

He walks through the corridor, with the sound of the bell, announcing one of the several services in the dining car, ringing somewhere behind or in front of him.

He has been seated at a table for four. The two seats by the window are occupied by a couple. Opposite him is a man about forty years old, an average Frenchman to judge by his clothing, who is nervously rolling his piece of bread into little balls.

There are various objects on the table: glasses, plates, knives, forks, and spoons. Next to him, on his right, is the obsessive sound of the conversation being carried on between the elderly couple, the general meaning of which escapes him. He tries not to listen.

THE WOMAN: If she hasn't managed to get in touch with Lucienne, the whole thing will be a catastrophe.
THE HUSBAND: Do you think so?

He takes the menu and glances at it, in order to be doing something. Anyway, he knows it by heart, considering all the times he's made this same trip.

THE WOMAN: How do you expect her to do it without Lucienne?
THE HUSBAND: Come now, she's used to it.

He puts down the menu and glances at his neighbors. He unfolds his napkin and waits.

THE WOMAN: At Royan last year she was used to it?
THE HUSBAND: It was different at Royan. She wasn't in her own home.

He sees the waiter coming with the bottles of wine and the mineral water.
They are eating.

THE WOMAN: If Lucienne left, believe me, it's not only to take care of her nephews. There's more to it than that.
THE HUSBAND: You're always making mountains out of mole-hills.
THE WOMAN: If I mention it, it's because I have reason to know. Now, of course, she's probably sorry about Lucienne.
THE HUSBAND: Do you think she didn't ask Lucienne to come?

He takes a sip of wine.

On the other side of the passageway that separates the rows of tables in the dining car, he sees a girl who reminds him of Nadine Sallanches, that is, of the image he projected of her in his mind's eye that morning. Seeing this dark-haired girl's face in actuality, with its expression of adolescent gravity, has set off a chain of free association.

Again he tries to imagine what Nadine looks like, from her voice and what he knows about her. He tries to situate her in her home environment, knowing as he does that she lives on the rue de l'Estrapade, in a building that must overlook the wall of the Lycée Henri IV. She must hang out in the cafés around the Place de la Contrescarpe, so close to where she lives. He pictures her, Nadine of a thousand faces, in this familiar setting.

Suddenly, the image of the Place de la Contrescarpe, with Nadine blurred, changing, elusive, merges into the memory of a July 14th celebration, with the drum and bugle corps of the Ecôle des Beaux Arts performing there on the square, the crowd happy, the Chinese lanterns, a woman walking toward him, a woman whose beauty is beginning to fade and who, as a result, becomes all the more moving, a beauty which, though it is beginning to fade, still blazes beneath the light of his gaze, the glitter of full lips. So close to him, suddenly.

*

The Woman's Voice has gone on and on, unendingly.

WOMAN'S VOICE: If the Marcels come, that makes two. The Andrés, two, unless they bring Pierre. Two or three. And then she herself. Raoul promised to come, at least for a day. And then her two daughters, the sons-in-law, and maybe even some of the grandchildren, the oldest ones. Can you imagine, feeding that whole crowd, doing the beds, keeping the house in order, all that without Lucienne being there? . . .

HUSBAND'S VOICE: But don't get so upset about it! You'll see that Lucienne's already there, she will have arrived before that whole crowd does.

WOMAN'S VOICE: The whole thing will be a catastrophe. If they didn't let Lucienne know, the whole thing will be a catastrophe!

He's eating a bombe glacée. *On the Sud-Express, there is always* bombe glacée *for dessert.*

THE HUSBAND: You're always imagining the worst. Just tell yourself we're going to a party and that we're going to enjoy seeing everyone again.

THE WOMAN: A party? And what if they all make long faces?

THE HUSBAND: Lucienne doesn't even belong to the family. You've got to try and keep some perspective.

THE WOMAN: So what? What if she isn't part of the family? But if she's not there, the family's going to be in a pretty state, mark my words!

II

The Truths of the Lie

IVRY, A SUBURB OF PARIS. Sunday, 5:30 P.M.

He arrives beneath a gray sky, covered with clouds whose fringes are shot through with rainbow-like colors from the rays of the setting sun.

He is carrying his handbag in his right hand. Perhaps he had his mind on other things, perhaps he was looking at the sky—at the iridescent clouds—but suddenly the houses are there.

We have already seen them before in his imagination, in that anticipated future with which he has filled his hours since morning. Now they are here, actual. Suddenly they impinge upon his gaze. Hard beside him, looming, settled there, needing nothing to be there, no look or gaze even, in their geometric uniformity. Some of the buildings, considerably taller than the five-story blocks of apartments which predominate, break up the alignment of this new city in the suburbs of Paris.

He takes a few more steps and is in the midst of the buildings. The place is deserted: only he and the buildings. Then a little girl passes by on her bicycle, endlessly ringing her bicycle bell. In the silence, the fading sound of the high-pitched bell seems to be measuring infinity.

He walks toward the nearest cluster of dwellings. At the entrance, the letter "E" in a dark color stands out in bas-relief on the granite-like cement. The door opens and a group of children dashes out, carrying some empty bottles. He lifts his eyes and counts the stories: five. Then he turns back toward the three tall towers which attempt to give the whole complex of buildings an aura of status.

The letter "D" is on the entranceway of the first tower; no, that's not yet it. He looks through the big bay windows into the lobby, at an elevator which has just arrived and is letting off two or three people.

The second tower bears the letter "G," and he goes into it. People are waiting in front of the elevator. Some are reading, others are merely waiting. No one turns to look at him.

Up to the eighth story, there are people getting off at their respective floors, but from the eighth to the tenth floor he is alone. There's no door on the elevator. He sees the grayish cement of the elevator shaft, the green metal door of the ninth floor, then more gray cement, and the elevator stops.

He pushes the door open. He is in a hexagonal-shaped area off which the hallways lead. Opposite him, a bay window: through it can be seen the new city, the cars entering and leaving the parking lot; a vast desert peopled by mechanical movements.

He wanders through the hallways, looking for a door. There are numbers on the doors. . . . He stops in front of 107. He rings.

The door opens, a woman is looking at him. Behind her, beyond that open door and another open door beyond, is the bluish, luminous glow of a television flickering, and the loud voices announcing some sports program.

CARLOS: Antonio sent me.

But this sentence, which should have provoked something, some reaction, some set reply, has no effect.

There is silence, insuperable silence, between this woman and him.

THE WOMAN: What?

She brushes her hair back with her hand and looks at him.

CARLOS: This is Madame Lopez', isn't it?
THE WOMAN: No, it's not. I'm Madame Pluvier: Bernadette Pluvier.

He looks at her, and going through his mind, why he doesn't know, is the thought that the name Bernadette suits her very well.

CARLOS: I beg your pardon. I was looking for Madame Lopez.
THE WOMAN: There's no Madame Lopez here.

He speaks mechanically.

CARLOS: Building "G," tenth floor, apartment 107.

She evinces surprise. Even a trace of anxiety, perhaps.

THE WOMAN: That's right. But there's no Madame Lopez here.

He looks around, disconcerted.

CARLOS: Then I must have made a mistake.

He begins to turn away from the door.

THE WOMAN: Who is this Madame Lopez, a refugee from Algeria?

At first he doesn't understand. He pauses on the threshold.

CARLOS: Refugee . . . ? Oh, no, I don't think so.
THE WOMAN: I thought perhaps, because of the name . . . There are lots of refugees living here.

Again, he begins to leave.

CARLOS: I beg your pardon.

He smiles. She looks at him, relaxed now. She is smiling too. The door closes. He sees three numbers on the door, which no longer mean anything: 107.

*

He is in front of the elevator, whose blinking red light indicates it is coming.

As usual, he is calm, self-possessed, not given to any useless movements: like someone who is doing his job, patiently.

The red light is blinking, obsessively, at regular intervals, and the images in his mind, red images, begin to blink as well: doors closing, the face of a woman (very precise, not just any woman; we shall meet her again very soon), the faces of men: Juan's face, of course, and also the thin, desiccated, very dark-skinned face of the man who, in his mental projections and premonitions, has accompanied him on his search for Juan.

As these images form and dissolve, the Narrator's Voice can be heard voice-over.

NARRATOR'S VOICE: A year ago you came to see Juan. Building "G," tenth floor, apartment 107, Madame Lopez's apartment. You think you remember. But now there's no Juan, no Madame Lopez. Maybe it was somewhere else, another building "G," another tenth floor.

Maybe Juan's already left. Juan's going to fall into the trap. . . . Roberto. You've got to find Roberto now.

*

The elevator is there, the door opens automatically. The red light stops blinking, the images stop blinking too. He gets into the elevator.

AUBERVILLIERS, ANOTHER SUBURB OF PARIS. Sunday, 7:00 P.M.

Later, somewhere else.

Another near suburb of Paris: Aubervilliers. Another cluster of government-subsidized apartment houses.

He gets out of the bus.

He glances around, his handbag still in his hand, as though he were trying to get his bearings, to remember a route he's already traveled, but not often enough for him to recall it automatically.

He finds his bearings and sets off among the cluster of buildings. He remembers the way, but only after a certain number of hesitations and a certain amount of backtracking.

NARRATOR'S VOICE: She's going to wonder what's wrong, she's

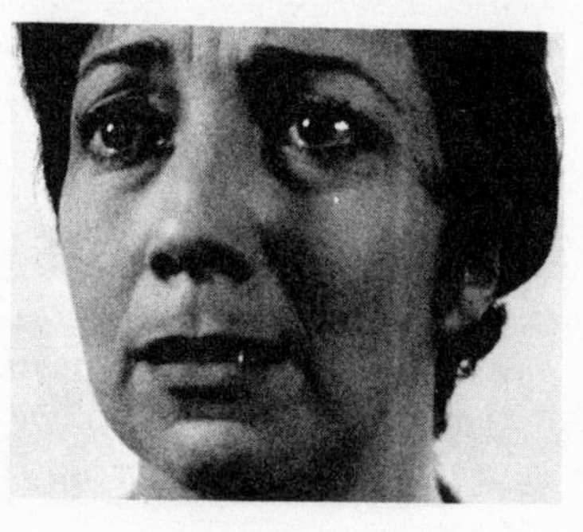

going to understand that something's happened to her husband. You would have preferred not to see her today. But you needed her, she's the one who can take you to Roberto's house. Last Thursday, Andrés failed to show up at the appointed time, at 6:00 P.M., at the Botanical Gardens. You had a beer at the bar of the Café Nacional. It was nothing, not yet anyway, you would see Andrés the next day, at the rescue meeting. Toward nightfall, though, the danger signs were out. The comrade who operates the print shop failed to come home. His brother alerted the others. There were other signs, other people who disappeared. The airtight world in which we live became moving, unsettled, full of traps.

He starts up a stairway, walks up two flights, looks at the two doors on each landing. On one of the two doors, which he examines closely, is the tiny glass spyhole which allows the person inside to see who is in the hallway without being seen: that's the door.

He rings.

He is opposite this tiny glass eye which he is staring at, which is staring at him. Behind that glazed eye, set into the door, he imagines another real, living eye which could be watching him: a forehead, a face around that eye. The face of the woman he expects to find behind that door, that he is hoping to find behind that door. The face of the woman which appeared to him a while back when he was staring at the red blinking light of the elevator.

Suddenly the door opens toward the interior. The door opens abruptly, as if the person who was standing behind that door, who was watching him, was surprised or moved or worried when she recognized him, and that surprise, that emotion, or that concern had impelled her to open the door quickly.

The face of the woman that he had hoped to find is there, the real face, alive.

She is a woman of average height, with signs of energy visible on her face, which is careworn, marked by life, her hair already gray, unkempt, constantly falling down over her face. She looks at him with surprise, perhaps with concern. In any case, she did not expect to see him, and his appearance has, perhaps, some special significance. She looks at him, at his handbag.

CARLOS: Carmen!

He has not pronounced her name with a French accent, that is, with the accent on the last syllable, but with a Spanish accent, emphasizing the first syllable of her name. Carmen steps back to let him in.

CARMEN: Estàs aqui?

She has said: "You, here?" because the fact that he is there is abnormal, unusual at least, because he ought to be somewhere else, in Madrid, because she knows that in principle he was in Madrid.

*

The living room typical of these government-subsidized apartments.

A vinyl covering on the floor. A scattering of modern furniture, sub-functional, that is, inexpensive imitations of the kind of furniture known as functional. A fairly old-model television, with "rabbit's-ears" antennae on top. In the background, large bay windows with, dimly perceived, other apartment buildings beyond.

But this general view is not enough. Now we must explore this tiny universe, this life frozen in the objects which people this banal space: the books, the photographs, everything else.

Now we must see, must look at, coldly but tenderly (is it possible to have a look at this tiny universe of exile which is both tender and cold, at the long tragic profession of political exile? in any case we must make the attempt), the table next to the bay window, with the typewriter on it, the stencil begun, at the pile of Spanish papers piled on it. We must understand that Carmen was in the process of typing a stencil containing the important extracts from the Spanish papers, to be run off on a mimeograph machine. And this work, on Sunday, will situate Carmen in a certain place in a certain world of projects, activities, and of dreams too.

Now we must look on the shelf, in the corner over the bed, at that collection of pot-bellied, Russian baba dolls, of every kind and color, squeezed tightly one against the other, placed there in ascending or descending order according to height, depending on whether you looked from right to left or left to right.

Now we must look at the few books arranged at the head, or at the foot, of this same couch, where the shelves placed one above the other form a kind of small library. We must scrutinize these books, at least certain of them, and read, puzzle out, their titles.

Now we must listen while we explore, tenderly and with infinite care, this tiny universe cut off from the world but in which the real problems of the world are reflected, listen to the voices of this man who is forty and of this woman who must be about the same age, more or less, this man and this woman who belong to the same universe, the same undertaking: a slow, stubborn, and indeterminate undertaking.

CARMEN'S VOICE: Pasa algo?

This voice is asking whether something's the matter.

This Spanish voice, full of anxiety, is asking whether something is wrong (only two words, two everyday words, insignificant when taken individually but which now explode, revealing the woman's anxiety), while the camera, now motionless, is frozen on some customary, or seemingly customary, object in the room (the typewriter) which is going to become (because of this immobility of the image and the anxiety-ridden voice) itself disturbing, suddenly offering some insight into a world fraught with the possibilities of danger and suffering.

We hear this anxious voice off-screen, we see this frozen image, and then silence. There is no answer to that question.

The visual image becomes unfrozen, the camera begins to move again along the surfaces, bright or dull in the evening light, of the objects and furniture in this room.

Andrés? Qué le pasa a Andrés.

This woman's voice is asking what has happened to Andrés, whether something has happened to Andrés.

They appear now, in this room previously peopled only by objects, by a human presence materialized in these objects. They appear, he standing, his face inscrutable, having said nothing as yet, not knowing how to tell this woman that arrests have been made in Madrid, and that her husband was among those arrested.

And she backs away, away from him, having understood what had happened to her husband, to Andrés, having gathered it from the man's silence, from his expressionless face, his obvious inability to speak, backing away, having understood that, backing away, her hands covering her face, paralyzed by fear, having at last attained that pain, that suffering which for so many years had been feared and expected, ever since her husband, Andrés, had been engaged in this clandestine work; a suffering which would wake you up in the middle of the night, your heart pounding, a prey to some terrible foreboding, which now has become not real—it always was real—but actual, that is, justified by the facts.

Backing away, as though forced to do so by some irresistible force, toward the sofa, a chair, anything to lean on or where one can find a respite from the feeling that one's legs are going to give way. Backing away, beneath the pressure of that force, of that sudden weakness, until a wall, or some solid obstacle, blocks her flight, stops her and keeps her motionless, her hands over her face, becoming aware of her sudden solitude, for now she is alone in the field of vision, not beautiful but ground down by life, by the daily fears which have prepared and nurtured, over a span of many years, today's sorrow: motionless, frozen, only her hands are moving, like frightened birds, over her face, her shoulders, through her hair, the strands of which keep falling down over her face, nervously fingering her dress, until a long sob escapes from her lips, a sob without tears, a harsh, stifled sob: a long-drawn-out moan.

And from the moment she began to back away, struck by that news she guessed, read in the eyes of this man, in his expressionless face, the Narrator's Voice is heard, voice-over:

NARRATOR'S VOICE: Friday, it became obvious that Andrés had disappeared, and Luis, and Justo, and Ricardo. Behind the scenes, in the shadow we began to strike back against that unforeseeable progression of the police roundups, cutting the ties that bound one group to another, this sector to that, suspending all meetings, all contacts, setting up new systems of liaison. But Andrés had disappeared, he has disappeared. For fifteen years he could have disappeared any day, and Carmen had expected it, foreseen it, accepted it ahead of time with a mixture of anger and anxiety, accepted this disappearance which now bursts upon her, today. . . . Thursday evening, at 6:00 P.M., Andrés did not show up for the appointment at Botanical Gardens. . . .

Carmen's hands, like frightened birds, move over her face, over her mouth, which can no longer contain this long sob which, harsh and stifled, bursts forth, this long moan, without tears.

*

Aubervilliers; evening; the lights are on.

It is a Sunday evening in spring, the streets are crowded, with people out walking, lining up in front of the cinema, the sound of music.

Through this real Sunday universe, Carmen and the Passenger are walking. He is still carrying his handbag.

NARRATOR'S VOICE: But you must rouse her from this sorrow, this solitude. She knows where to find Roberto, today, in this Sunday at Aubervilliers, among all these houses which empty as the weekend draws to a close, among all these Sunday night lights. Roberto's the one who arranges the trips. He's the only one who will know where to find Juan. He's the only one who can catch Juan before he too disappears.

They are lost in the Sunday crowd at Aubervilliers, as they walk quickly, purposefully, through the crowd, through the Sunday night sounds.

ISSY-LES-MOULINEAUX. Sunday, 8:10 P.M.

Roberto's face.

He is the short, thin, desiccated, dark-skinned man with whom, in his imagination, projected toward the future, Carlos had gone looking for Juan.

Roberto, in a taxi, leans over the front seat: he is paying the driver.

Carlos is standing on the sidewalk, holding the door, watching him pay the driver.

Now night has fallen, in the dappled sweetness of spring.

Roberto has gotten out of the car.

As the taxi pulls away, they each light a cigarette.

Then, when the taxi has turned the corner, they start walking.

In silence they skirt the wall of the old cemetery in Issy. When they pass the gate, Carlos glances at it. Farther along, there is a quiet street, more provincial than suburban: small outdated private homes, some of them actually in disrepair, set back at the far end of their meager gardens, which in certain cases show signs of loving care. As they walk, we hear the Narrator's Voice:

NARRATOR'S VOICE: Roberto detests bad news. His temper wears thin whenever there are any arrests, not only because friends have fallen, not only because months of work must be started over again from scratch: he gets upset because the reality of the world resists us, because he saw what we did as being a dream of indefinite progress. He hates it when reality fails to coincide with his dream. And he almost blames you, as though you were the malicious messenger of this unforeseeable, impenetrable reality.

They open the gate to one of these houses, which has a kind of shed or garage attached to one side, and walk in.

*

A shed, or workshop, slightly longer than it is wide, with a very high ceiling. At one end, a large wooden door, closed by a thick, solid iron bar.

On the opposite wall, a cement walkway runs along its entire width, about waist high. At one end of this walkway is a door leading into the house. At the other, a fairly steep iron stairway leading down to the cement floor of the shed, which is covered with spots of oil. The two other walls are covered with long, solid shelves, on which are piled the most disparate variety of objects: a great number of suitcases of varying sizes and shapes; hand luggage, briefcases, women's handbags. There are also, seen from the other side, all sorts of wooden planks of various sizes and thicknesses. Along one of the walls, spanning its entire length, is a workbench, with a lathe and all kinds of tools.

In the center of the shop is a car, beneath which a man is working with a soldering iron. Both rear doors of the car have been removed and are leaning against the door frames. The interior padding of both doors has been removed.

A woman, who is leading the way for the two men, has started walking along the cement walkway, coming from the door of the house itself, which has remained open.

Under the car, we can see the sparks made by the blow-torch.

WOMAN'S VOICE: Ramon!

She has pronounced the name à l'espagnole, *but the faintest trace of an accent in her manner of rolling her "r" makes us understand that she is French.*

The sputter of the blowtorch stops, and a man works his way out from beneath the car. He takes off his welder's glasses and looks.

The woman is descending the steps of the iron staircase and the two men are standing motionless on the walkway.

RAMON'S WIFE: Ramon! You have visitors!

She has spoken very loudly, as she did the first time. But then the noise of the blowtorch all but drowned out her voice. Now, in the silence, her voice resounds and reverberates in the echoing silence of the large shop.

Ramon looks at the two men standing on the walkway, leaning on the railing.

RAMON: I'll be damned! Carlos!

With almost no transition, Ramon turns to his wife who is walking toward him.

Why are you shouting?

But he doesn't wait for her reply. He has set down the blow-torch, which he was still holding in his hand. He is standing on the cement floor of the shop, a broad smile on his face.

Ramon must be about fifty. He is tall, thin, very solidly built. His hair is completely gray.

Carlos, what are you doing here?

He walks over to the man he has called Carlos. They embrace each other, as Spaniards do.

Ramon steps back and looks at Carlos.

You've put on weight.

CARLOS: I'm getting old, the easy life . . .

They laugh.

But the short, dark, dessicated man who has accompanied Carlos breaks in.

ROBERTO: Juan get away all right this morning?

He too has spoken in French, but with a heavy Spanish accent.

RAMON: Juan? He left at noon. I finished his car last night. He left at noon.

Ramon's wife is standing motionless, watching her husband over the top of the car.

Then Carlos' face contracts, his eyes close for a second. So the fact remains he has arrived too late. In the darkness of his closed eyes, the dizzying image of Juan's face lights up, but without really taking shape or becoming clear.

He opens his eyes again.

CARLOS: What route did he take?

Ramon looks at him, trying to figure what relevance that question might have.

RAMON: Perpignan.

He turns to Roberto.

Wasn't he first going to Barcelona?

ROBERTO: Yes, to Barcelona.

Carlos' mind has been working as he listened to them. He comes back to his original idea.

CARLOS: He only left at noon? When is he supposed to cross the border? Where is he spending the night?

Ramon looks at him, carefully, trying to understand why he seems so concerned. Roberto looks at him too, but with an air of annoyance. Perhaps he even makes some movement which reveals his irritation.

RAMON: He's spending the night at Perpignan. Tomorrow morn-ning at ten he'll be introduced to the person who will be picking him up in two weeks in Madrid. After that he'll cross the border.

Carlos turns to Roberto.

CARLOS: Really? Then we can warn him. Bring him back to Paris.

Both he and Roberto are standing on the crosswalk. Ramon and his wife are looking at them from below: they still don't understand what it's all about.

Roberto shrugs his shoulders.

ROBERTO: There's no point.

He looks at the faces of Ramon and his wife, raised toward him.

Anyhow, it's too late.

CARLOS: What do you mean? You don't mean to say there isn't some place you can call them in Perpignan?

His voice is one degree louder.

ROBERTO: Telephoning would be dangerous.

Roberto's remark was dry and sententious. It's obvious he does not like to have anyone telling him what he should do. Carlos' laugh is short and aggressive.

CARLOS: Listen, let's not exaggerate. We can send a telegram. And besides, if you don't want to run any risk, one of us can still catch the evening train and be in Perpignan in plenty of time.

Roberto mechanically glances at his watch. Then he looks at Carlos.

ROBERTO: Mira, no te pongas nervioso. Mañana por la mañana nos reunimos con los camaradas.

Till now they've all been speaking French, because of the presence of Ramon's wife. And also because after so many years of exile they often fall into the habit of speaking French among themselves, integrated as they are into French life. But Roberto has just lapsed into Spanish, perhaps because he wants this discussion to come to an end. He has told Carlos not to sweat it, that he'll call a meeting of the comrades for the following morning.

Carlos again laughs, a brief, cutting laugh.

CARLOS: Nervioso?

He is astonished that anyone can think he is nervous. Again he gives a short laugh, this time looking squarely at the short, swarthy man.

*

Beyond this face, there is Juan's face, Juan's profile, in a car which is going up a winding road toward Perthus, toward the border checkpoint.

But why is Juan being driven by Mr. Jude, the bookseller from Hendaye? Carlos erases from his mind the mental image of Mr. Jude. Now there is only Juan's face, seen in profile.

*

RAMON'S WIFE: But what's happening today? Why does Juan have to come back?

Carlos turns to Ramon and his wife. He begins walking toward them as he speaks.

CARLOS: He mustn't go to Madrid. There have been raids, arrests are being made.
RAMON: Who have they arrested?
CARLOS: Andrés. And three others from the Madrid committee. The printer's also been arrested. And when I left it was still going on.
RAMON'S WIFE: Andrés? Have you told Carmen?

Carlos turns to her and nods. They remain motionless, not speaking. Roberto in turn leaves the walkway.

ROBERTO: We'll have to wait for more details before we can judge whether the situation is really serious.

Carlos turns to him. His voice betrays a certain exasperation.

CARLOS: I've given you the news up to last night. That ought to be enough.

ROBERTO: You know as well as I that people tend to exaggerate at first. It's only normal: at the first sign of trouble, they see everything falling apart.

He reverts to his sententious air.

They're too close to things to see the situation clearly.

CARLOS: You mean to say that here, two thousand kilometers away, we can see them more clearly?

He has made every effort to load his words with irony. But Roberto refuses to be dissuaded.

ROBERTO: That's right, we have a clearer perspective.

He makes an expansive gesture as he speaks, but Ramon breaks in.

RAMON: And what about Juan?

ROBERTO: Don't worry about him. We have three days. He's staying in Barcelona till Wednesday evening.

CARLOS: In Perpignan he'd be even safer. I'll take the responsibility for this decision: we'll keep him in Perpignan.

He has spoken in loud and peremptory tones. But Roberto replies in the same manner.

ROBERTO: I'm in charge of the trips. He's got important things to do in Barcelona. And now every minute counts.

CARLOS: Every minute? Have you people in Paris gone stark raving mad? For the past twenty-five years every minute's counted!

ROBERTO: Why are you talking about twenty-five years, when the general strike's been called for twelve days from now? And this year May 1st is no joke. That's why every minute counts!

CARLOS: May 1st comes around every year, but Juan won't. If he's caught, he'll get twenty years. You know that as well as I do. . . . As for the general strike, we can discuss that at tomorrow's meeting.

The tension between them is strikingly apparent; almost physical. Ramon tries to ease the tension by interjecting a new thought.

RAMON: In any case, if you need someone to go to Barcelona, I'm your man. It'll get me out of my rut.

He makes a broad gesture, indicating the shop.

RAMON'S WIFE: Out of your rut? Is your wife part of that rut? You mean you want a change of air?

Ramon looks at his wife with a mixture of admiration and tenderness.

RAMON: They're extraordinary, these Breton women. I offer to go on a secret trip to help a friend in danger, and it's as though I were suggesting taking a vacation!

All four of them laugh. Perhaps the reason why Ramon and his wife have exchanged this banter was to make them laugh, to relax the tension.

Carlos turns to Roberto.

CARLOS: Si hay que ir a Barcelona, yo mismo, serà lo màs ràpido.

He says that he'll go to Barcelona himself: that would be the quickest. But Roberto shakes his head, he says he'll have to think it over.

ROBERTO: Veremos, ya veremos.

Ramon's wife wants to take advantage of this easing of the tension, to prolong it.

RAMON'S WIFE: You're not going to stand here all night? Come on in the house and let me give you something to drink.

Ramon turns to her.

RAMON: That's a good idea, bring us something to drink, but bring it here. I have to finish this car.

The three of them remain standing in the shop, as Ramon turns back to his work. He's in the process of loading the insides of the doors with tracts of propaganda printed in tiny type on Bible paper. He slips the tracts in between the metal exteriors of the doors and the upholstered interiors, which at present have been removed, then fastens them there with scotch tape. It's obvious he's had long experience with this kind of job: his movements are rapid and efficient. He has finished filling the first interior, and proceeds to screw the door upholstery back into place.

Carlos and Roberto watch him work, without speaking. The former is seated on a wooden box, the latter on the edge of the workbench.

As soon as Ramon has finished screwing the upholstery back into place, they both get up, as if by a signal, and go over to help him remount the door on its hinges.

For a brief moment they are united in their common effort, coordinating their movements.

*

On one corner of the workbench that has been cleared away, there is a tray with glasses, plates with slices of bright red Spanish "chorizo," olives, either very green and tart or a brownish black, small pieces of bread on which pieces of dry cheese have been impaled on toothpicks: Swiss and cantal cheese.

A hand picks up a piece of bread and cheese, and Carlos lifts the morsel to his mouth, then he puts the toothpick down on the tray and drinks a swallow of wine from a glass he takes from the workbench.

Ramon's wife is there, and Roberto. They are seated, drinking wine and nibbling at the olives, the "chorizo," and the bread and cheese.

RAMON'S WIFE: How did it start this time?

RAMON: As it always does, I suppose.

ROBERTO: That's right, the way it always does. It's always the same thing.

As he spoke these words he shrugged his shoulders.

CARLOS: Well, the fact is it wasn't the same as always.

Roberto has raised his head, attentive.

They struck the same day, at the same time, in several places at once. The print shop, the comrades involved in the propaganda apparatus, were all arrested at the same time. Andrés and Luis were caught in their secret residences. That's the first time that has happened.

Ramon has returned to his work. But Carlos' words worry him. He stops and looks at the others.

RAMON: You mean it might be dangerous for Juan if he were to go to Madrid?

CARLOS: It was in his area of responsibility they made the raid. He's been going there for years. He may have been spotted.

Roberto addresses him, almost aggressively.

ROBERTO: And what about you? Haven't you been going there for years too? And yet here you are, drinking red wine with us.

CARLOS: Luis' wife heard the police speaking among themselves while they were searching the apartment. They said they had a photo of one of the Paris leaders, a picture they'd taken in the street with a telephoto lens, and that they were sure they'd arrest him. They could only have been talking about Juan.

Now Roberto unleashes the full force of his anger.

ROBERTO: Don't you realize that all these stories of films and photographs are pure fabrication! The police spread these rumors to demoralize the opposition.

He turns to Carlos, and his gestures emphasize each of his words.

Thursday, the same day the arrests were made, you had an appointment with Andrés?

He paces back and forth. His tone of voice is one degree louder.

And yet here you are. Because there weren't any photos, and Andrés won't talk. It's very simple. They carried out a raid because they're afraid. Because they want to nip our preparations in the bud. They made a raid. So what? For twenty years now they've been making raids. That's the way war is: you strike blows against the enemy, and they strike back.

Again the tension is so thick you could cut it with a knife. Then Ramon's wife breaks in.

RAMON'S WIFE: Don't get so upset, Roberto.

Roberto looks at her and regains control of himself.

ROBERTO: I'm not excited. Just because I raise my voice doesn't mean I'm excited. It's just this crazy life we lead.

RAMON'S WIFE: It's gone on too long, that's what's crazy about it.

She's said this matter-of-factly, because that's what she thinks. Because it's true, it has gone on too long. But her eyes meet her husband's, and she's afraid he'll mistake her words for a recrimination. This is a subject they must have discussed often, and they look at each other. And in her look there is no recrimination, but tenderness: all the tenderness possible, and all the confidence and all the love and all the patience in the world. They look at each other, and they're alone, she reaches out her hand and places it on Ramon's, and he takes it and squeezes it, and they remain this way, their hands locked together.

Roberto goes over to Carlos.

ROBERTO: Bueno. Mañana por la mañana, a las ocho, en "Pierre Curie."

He's giving Roberto the time and place of the meeting tomorrow morning: eight o'clock, at the Pierre Curie Metro stop.

They part company. Carlos and Roberto are leaving. Ramon and Roberto walk ahead. Carlos walks behind, with Ramon's wife.

RAMON'S WIFE: Marianne must be expecting you.

Carlos shakes his head.

You didn't let her know you were coming?

She seems shocked.

CARLOS: She's probably not in Paris. And besides, I didn't come for her. I came for Juan. Yes, I'm sure she must be out of town.

RAMON'S WIFE: Why?

CARLOS: You mean you've forgotten it's Easter?

RAMON'S WIFE: You're quite right! I'd completely forgotten.

She's said this last without any trace of bitterness, rather with a laugh.

If you find the house empty, Carlos, you're always welcome to come back and spend the night here. It'll be more pleasant for you.

CARLOS: Maybe I will. I'll see.

*

He sees, in his mind's eye, the large empty room overlooking the Seine, which has previously appeared several times in his thoughts. And then, because he realizes that he must go see Nadine Sallanches, to straighten out the question of the telephone call that morning, a very rapid series of mental images follows: the rue de l'Estrapade, shots of the evanescent girls he had tried to imagine when he was trying to picture Nadine that morning.

AT NADINE SALLANCHES'. Sunday, 9:45 P.M.

He is climbing the broad stairway, whose steps have been polished by the centuries, of a very old and very handsome building.

Then, heralded by the click of high heels on the stone (like the sound of a sudden shower of hard rain on a roof), a girl descends the stairs. She keeps to the side near the banister, and Carlos steps aside to let her pass. She goes by without so much as glancing at him, or so it would seem. Carlos stops two or three steps higher up and turns around to look at the girl.

Just as he pivots to look back, the sound of her high heels, the patter of heavy rain on a tin roof, stops. The girl has also stopped, ten or twelve steps down, after the second story landing.

They are facing each other, he dominating the girl who looks up at this man she has just passed.

NADINE: Is it you?

Carlos smiles.

CARLOS: That all depends.

She starts back up the stairs, holding onto the railing, her eyes on his.

NADINE: Are you the person I talked to on the phone this morning?

Carlos watches her climb the stairs, slowly, drawn toward him.

CARLOS: Yes.

There is a brief silence, during which she continues to climb the stairs, lithe along the railing, facing him.

I recognize your voice.

Then, in an almost childlike reaction, she begins to dash up the stairs, her short hair fluttering, and she laughs. She reaches the step just below the one Carlos is standing on.

NADINE: I've waited for you until now.

She continues on up, moving around and beyond him. He turns and watches her, without moving from the same step. Again she is facing him, on that portion of the stairway beyond the half landing between the second and third floors. Now it is she who dominates him. She looks at him with a smile.

Come on.

They are in the foyer of Nadine's apartment.

CARLOS: Isn't your father home?

Nadine walks into the apartment. She turns around, with a serious expression.

NADINE: If he were here, God knows where you'd be.

He starts to follow her, and laughs at her remark.

CARLOS: You don't know how true that is.

She looks at him carefully, as though she were trying to figure him out, to size him up.

NADINE: Of course I know.

Her voice was clipped, harsh, no longer that of an adolescent.

*

The room is a well carpeted and curtained space in which the shadow of moving leaves is seen. It is a fairly large, rectangular room with a low ceiling. Through the open window, which looks onto an interior courtyard, drifts the rustle of the leaves of a big tree, which is close by. The room is a place wherein the recent souvenirs of childhood exist side by side with signs of an awakening interest in problems of the adult world. In one glass-enclosed case there are stuffed animals and dolls from various countries dressed in their various national costumes. Right next to it are two oversized photographs of Fidel Castro and Patrice Lumumba. Also the reproduction of a poster of the Commune of Paris.

It is a quiet room, and the shadows of the rustling leaves stir on the white square of the Commune poster.

The chairs and the girl's day bed are littered with various articles of clothing, which she picks up to allow them to sit down. He is standing, watching her come and go, open and close closets and dresser drawers.

NADINE: He asks if he can speak to my father. I tell him my father's away on a trip, which is the truth.

CARLOS: For once the truth served some useful purpose.

She stops and looks at him intently. In her hand she is holding some article of clothing she was going to put away.

NADINE: What happened at the border?

He shrugs his shoulders.

CARLOS: Nothing. A simple spot check, which they make from time to time. Mere routine. But they happened to pick us. That telephone call could have ruined everything.

NADINE: He said something about Spain, and I knew right away. My father had told me about his passport.

She smiles, pensive, lost in her thoughts.

In our family we have a weakness for Spain.

She again begins moving about, putting away her things. He is still standing, watching her.

Again Nadine's voice becomes precise, informative.

I pretended to be panic stricken, I asked all sorts of questions. I demanded that they let me speak to my father.

She laughs at the memory of the comic role she played, and again her laughter is childlike.

I must have been exemplary, the epitome of filial concern.

Carlos is leaning on the edge of the table.

CARLOS: In any case, you kept your composure. You got me out of a sticky situation.

She makes a gesture which is a mixture of irony and a hint at something, an allusion to some aspect of her existence.

NADINE: It's not the first time.

He looks at her, perhaps wondering to what she is referring. But he asks no questions.

There is a moment's silence. Suddenly, they both find themselves prey to a silence that grows heavier. They were, in a way, bound by the morning's incident, by that telephone call, the sound of their voices. Now that this relationship has been clarified and their curiosity satisfied, a certain level has been reached in their relationship. The heavy silence reveals the indeterminate nature of that relationship, which is at a turning point: can it develop and grow, or will it wither and end?

In any event, the silence is heavy.

CARLOS: And what about me? Did I play my role of the affectionate father well?

It's obvious that he's saying the first thing that comes to mind, in order to end the silence. It's also obvious that his words sound forced.

Nadine looks at him blankly, with no expression on her face.

NADINE: Whenever my father feels in an affectionate mood, he doesn't call me "darling."

She pauses briefly so that the end of her sentence is all the more forceful, so there is no ambiguity, to show clearly that she does not appreciate him playing this "papa bit" with her.

He calls me Nana.

Is there the hint of a challenge in these words? Again, after this ridiculous effort to break the silence, it settles down once more.

Nadine, having removed her shoes, has gone over and sat down on the couch. In the silence between them, they look at each other, then quickly turn away.

CARLOS: This border incident is of no consequence, I'm quite sure. But nevertheless, let's assume they send someone here to make further inquiries. When is your father coming back?

He has spoken in a precise, professional manner. Actually, he didn't come simply out of curiosity, or because he was intrigued by the voice of this girl. He came because his work demands that he clarify this passport matter, that he examine all the possible ramifications of the border incident he was involved in that morning.

NADINE: Tomorrow night.
CARLOS: Tomorrow? Monday?

He stops to think.

Then he has to have his passport back, with his photo in it. So he can show it, in case he has to.

He moves away from the table he was leaning on, or, rather, half sitting on. He crosses the room. He is leaving.

It'll be ready. I'll bring it by tomorrow afternoon.

He takes a few more steps, toward her, to say good-by.

NADINE: Are you leaving?

She seems surprised, or disappointed, that he is leaving.

He nods. Then she jumps to her feet and leans on him while she slips on her shoes, which were at the foot of the couch.

If I hurry I can make the ten o'clock show.

She has her shoes on, and is looking for her handbag. He is already next to the door.

She has found her bag. She goes toward him.

What do you do for a living? I mean, besides this.

He looks at her; he is struck by her youth.

CARLOS: Nothing.
NADINE: Have you always done this?
CARLOS: Always.
NADINE: And what did you do before?

He laughs. This childish interrogation amuses him.

CARLOS: That's a long time ago. I guess I wanted to be a writer, like everybody else.
NADINE: Don't say that! What you're doing is much more interesting!

She bursts out laughing. Now she is standing beside him, on the threshold; he is holding the door open.

In a nutshell, you're a professional revolutionary.
CARLOS: That's right, you hit the nail on the head.

Perhaps he's thinking of the things this term "professional revolutionary" evoke in his mind. In any case, he seems pensive.

NADINE: A real professional. Yes, I bet it's great to be a real pro.

His eyes bring him closer to her. They both laugh.

How do they work these passports? Can't they tell that the photograph's been changed?
CARLOS: It's impossible to tell. They would have to check in the police files to see whether the photograph is right or not. And they don't have these photo files at the border posts.

NADINE: Can I see?

He looks at her and shrugs his shoulders. He takes his hand off the door, which gently closes. He takes the passport out of his coat pocket. She comes over and stands on his left, right next to him, to look at the passport. He turns the pages of the passport, and she looks at the page where the photograph of René Sallanches ought to be, and where the photograph of Carlos now is. She looks at Carlos' photograph.

In other words, you could be my father.

She laughs, and this time there is something provocative about it.

Carlos turns to her, and Nadine's face is an inch away from his.

CARLOS: That's right, Nana.

She raises her head and kisses him on the mouth.

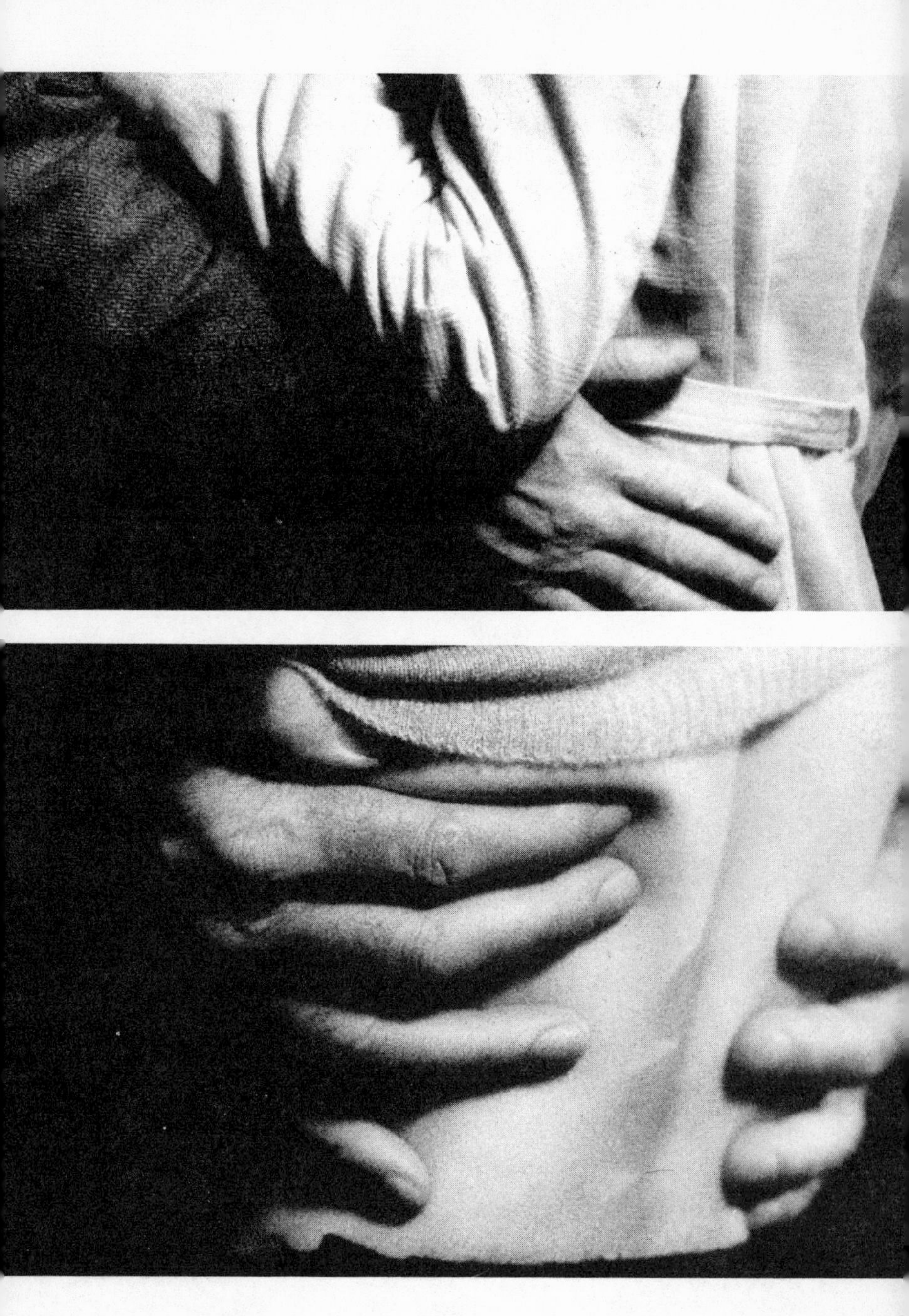

The room is well curtained and carpeted, and the shadows of the leaves stir on the unmade bed.

On the unmade bed, the shadows of the leaves, moving, rustling.

On Carlos' face, the shadows of the leaves, moving.

Carlos is seated on the unmade bed, the moving shadows of the leaves playing over his motionless face, which is turned toward the closed window.

His face is expressionless, reflecting neither joy nor even physical satisfaction.

His motionless face perhaps reveals a tremendous moral weariness, the weariness that follows exaltation when this exaltation is without any future as without any past, without tenderness, complicity or verbal exchange, when it has been the sudden, overwhelming exaltation of the present, of the moment offered and taken: nothing else. Not anything else, nothing more, nothing less.

Then things begin to stir.

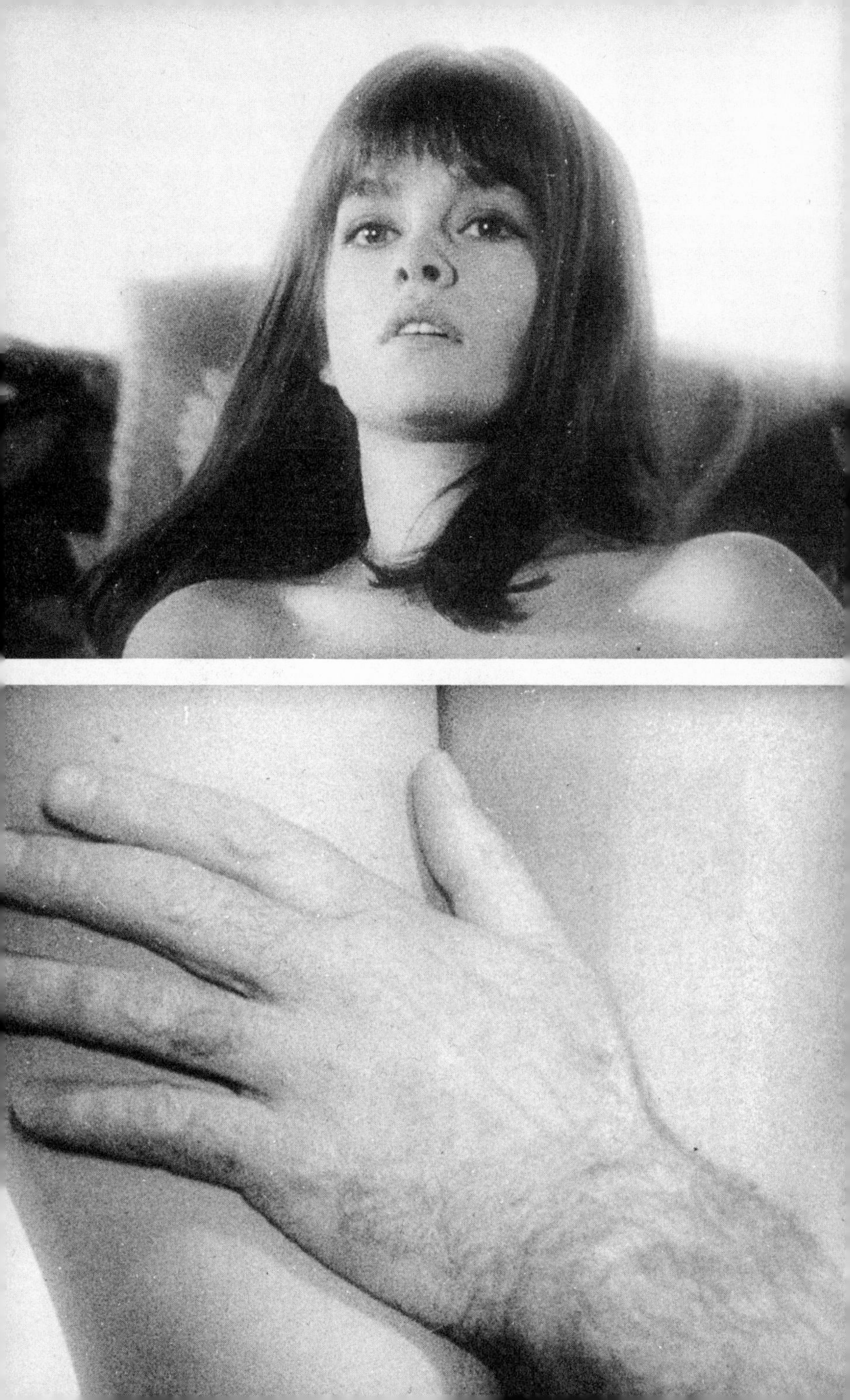

Not only the shadows of the foliage, which move everywhere. Things come to life, as it were. That is, objects, beings, rediscover their living soul, their life.

Carlos has bent over and is tying his shoelaces. He is in his shirtsleeves, with no tie.

A door opens, another door, not the door through which they were on the point of leaving when Nadine wanted to see the passport.

Nadine appears, barefoot, clothed in a billowing dressing gown, which should be white if she is a brunette.

She runs into the room, the dressing gown opening to bare her long, lovely legs. She flops down on the bed, lying on her belly, reaches for a cigarette on the night table, finds it, reaches for a lighter, lights her cigarette, and takes a long puff.

She rolls over closer to Carlos, who has turned to his right to look at her.

She laughs, snuggled up next to him. She can no longer see his face, which is still motionless, without expression.

Without looking at her, perhaps mechanically, he caresses her short hair, the nape of her neck.

He gets up, reaches for his tie, begins to tie it, while standing in front of her.

NADINE: Are you leaving?

He nods.

CARLOS: Yes.

He moves, to pick up his jacket, which he slips on as he walks back over to her.

NADINE: Is someone expecting you?
CARLO: Yes.

A silence. She is looking at him.

He comes over and sits down on the edge of the bed, he takes the cigarette from Nadine's lips, takes two long puffs, and puts it back in her mouth.

NADINE: What's your real name.
CARLOS: Sometimes, when I hear my real name, I jump.
NADINE: What is it?

He leans down over her and kisses her lightly on the lips. He's not going to tell the truth, obviously.

*

When he bent down over her, when he touched her lips, with his eyes closed, a rapid sequence of images passed through his mind, though each was slow in its own rhythm. A lightning-like succession of slow-motion shots: the Place de la Contrescarpe on a July 14th (to judge by the strings of Chinese lanterns and one's memory of the July 14th open-air dances), and this woman's face, walking toward him, beautiful with a beauty that is beginning to fade and which, for this very reason, becomes all the more lovely, a beauty past its peak but which is still in full bloom, beneath the observer's intent gaze, the burst of full lips. So close to him, suddenly.

*

But it is Nadine he has just kissed, and who has asked him what his name is.

He moves back from her.

CARLOS: Domingo.
NADINE: Which means "Sunday."
CARLOS: Right you are.
NADINE: How do you do, Sunday?

He's on his feet now, ready to leave.

CARLOS: What time tomorrow, for the passport?
NADINE: After lunch. But no later than three-thirty. I have to meet someone.

He is standing, ready to leave, looking at her.

Tonelessly, very rapidly, he recites the following as though he were repeating it by heart: in fact, he is repeating it by heart.

CARLOS: Nadine Sallanches: born October 26, 1944, completed her secondary studies at the Lycée Fénelon, speaks fluent English and Spanish, beginning her first year of university studies, literature major, lives alone with her father, a civil engineer employed by the government, who is often away because of his work. Dark hair, brown eyes, five feet five inches tall, operated on for appendicitis three years ago. . . .
NADINE: Say! You're a stickler for details!
CARLOS: Yes, we're finicky about details. It's the total picture we sometimes lose sight of.

For a second he is lost in thought, elsewhere. Then he leans down and lightly caresses her hair.

See you tomorrow.
NADINE: Good night, Sunday!

QUAI DE BETHUNE. Monday, 12:30 A.M.

He is abandoned, cast out into the night.

There had been the search for Juan, with its intimate tension constantly propelling him toward the future.

There had been the argument lost with Roberto. He had failed to have his way, impose his opinion. "I'm in charge of the trips," Roberto had said, and that was all.

There had been Nadine, but Nadine had been but the desire and pleasure of the moment. Not happiness unsatisfied—because of its inexhaustible wealth—but fleeting satisfaction: perhaps, above all, male pride flattered.

He's alone in the night, left alone in the night.

There are no mental intimations of a future, even a vague one, nor is there yet any memory. He is totally immersed in the nocturnal present.

He is in a street—the rue Cardinal Lemoine—walking toward a river—the Seine. A street, a river, a bridge, the sound of footsteps, in the total limpidity of the present. This is what is called anxiety, or solitude—true solitude—or the certainty of death.

But it is not necessary to explain things; it is enough simply to depict them: a street, a night, a river, a sound of footsteps, shadow, light: the present.

And yet he goes home.

But does he really have a home? Has he ever been home since he left his country? He comes back to the place he lives: a livable place, no more, no less.

After crossing the pont de Sully, he turned left onto the Ile Saint-Louis, the quai de Béthune, and the first street on his right, the rue de Bretonvilliers.

He has not raised his head to see whether there were any lights on, the way one does when one comes home hoping to see the lights lighted, the house inhabited. The lights of the lares and penates.

He is before an apartment door.

In his left hand, he is holding his handbag.

With his right hand, he caresses for a long time the worn and polished wood of the door; the way a blind man would, gropingly. As though he were trying to rediscover the depth and breadth of reality, the material history of the world inscribed in this smooth surface, worn away by time.

He takes a key from his pocket and opens the door to the apartment.

He expected to find an empty apartment, with no lights on. Actually, just as the door begins to open, the minuterie *light goes out in the hallway. For a fraction of a second, he finds himself in darkness.*

But he does not move from the darkness of the night outside, from the darkness of the stairway, into the darkness of an empty apartment. By the time the door is completely open, we can see that this apartment he thought was empty is brightly lighted. The open door also reveals certain sounds: a murmur of quiet voices, the rustle of objects being moved about, and, beyond these sounds, muffled but distinct enough to make out, the clearly recognizable sound of the Goldberg Variations.

He is in the apartment foyer, having closed the door behind him: slightly disconcerted. Feeling perhaps like an intruder in his own house, that is, in the place where he lives. He stands stock-still, listening.

The sound of a woman's footsteps is heard, just as he is about to move away from the big room from which the sounds are emanating and turn down a hallway leading off to the right.

A woman is standing on the threshold of the door leading into the room from which the sounds are coming, a woman who runs toward him.

MARIANNE: Diego!

This is the first time anyone has called him by this name since the day began. The first time he has been called by his real name. For it is his real name, without any doubt.

A little while ago he said his name was Domingo—which was a rather obvious lie, since today is Sunday.

But now this woman has called him by his real name. This woman, who knows the secret of his name, the keys to his life, the truth of his lie, this woman comes over to him and nestles in his arms, she takes his face in her hands as though once again she were, by this gesture, inventing this face, and she snuggles against him and cries out:

You!

She presses herself tightly against him, and he can't refrain from glancing past her face into the room from which the music and muffled sounds are coming. Now, though, the sounds have stopped. She sees him looking.

I'm not alone.

She states the obvious the way someone does who isn't quite sure what to say.

We're working.

Then he laughs.

DIEGO: And to think I've been putting off coming home. I was sure you'd be out of Paris.

They both laugh at this.

MARIANNE: Nobody told me you were coming.
DIEGO: No one knew. It wasn't planned.

He draws her to him, and with the tip of his finger traces the outline of her face, her eyebrows, the arc of her forehead, her cheeks, the line of her mouth.

MARIANNE: Diego!
DIEGO: Yes?
MARIANNE: That's all: I'm saying your name.

She says his name, to exorcize the long wait, the absence, the worry. She nestles closer in his arms.

You're here, I'm happy.

But his face betrays no expression.

DIEGO: I can't stay.

Actually, he's not sure he has to leave. Everything depends on tomorrow's meeting. But one has the impression he wants to dissipate any ambiguity immediately. As though he did not want the illusion of happiness to be created.

MARIANNE: You're leaving?
DIEGO: Tomorrow.

They are there, motionless, in each other's arms, but already separated. As though the announcement of an imminent departure was going to disunite them.

But what does disunite them is a foreign presence, whose gaze they feel upon them.

A young woman, beautiful, blonde, and glittering—has emerged from the big room and is looking at them, with an obvious, almost impolite curiosity.

They are there, separated by this woman's gaze.

Marianne is remiss in her role as mistress of the house. She gestures vaguely and makes what amounts to an introduction.

MARIANNE: You know Agnes?
DIEGO: No.

Almost dryly.

MARIANNE: I thought you'd already met.
DIEGO: No, I don't think so.

He is more relaxed.

AGNES: No, I assure you we haven't.
MARIANNE: You never saw Agnes at the office?

Diego makes a gesture expressing a certain irritation and the notion that he is helpless to answer such a question. Agnes is looking at Diego.

AGNES: No, we've never met. And anyhow, it's impossible. Diego is always away on a trip.

DIEGO: Always?

AGNES: In any case, ever since I've been working with Marianne, each time I've tried to wangle an introduction, you were away on a trip. I even began to wonder whether you really existed.

DIEGO: Well, now you can see I really do exist.

He seems utterly exhausted. He takes a few steps, moving away from them, toward the hallway. Agnes is looking at him go, with an expression of curiosity that borders on the indecent.

Marianne reacts.

MARIANNE: Stay with us for a bit, we've just finished.

She moves about, she speaks, she flutters around Diego.

Janine and Bill are here. They'll be so pleased to see you. We're preparing a book on cities, on all the cities of the world, I mean, on the way cities speak to people and the way people, the people in the street, react. We want to show how this dialogue becomes a language. It's complicated to explain, but in pictures it's quite simple. You'll see: we're using Bill's pictures and mixing them with drawings by Folon and Topor. I'm doing the dummy, together with Agnes. Bill's leaving for Brazil, so we immediately made an initial choice of his pictures before he left. We're taking advantage of the Easter holiday. We set up shop here, where we can have a little peace and quiet. They won't understand if you don't come in and say hello to them.

She introduces reassuring landmarks into this uncertain universe: it's an ordinary Easter Sunday, he's just got back from a trip, some friends are there—it's all very simple.

Diego looks at her and smiles.

*

They are in the large room, around a broad low coffee table on which are scattered photographs and the embryo of a book dummy.

Janine and Bill are there: obviously pleased to see him.

Janine and Bill are standing, looking at Diego who is bent over the table examining the photographs.

Agnes is slightly off to one side, watching Diego.

Marianne is moving about: she brings in some clean glasses.

Don't you want something to eat, Diego?

He answers without turning around, still looking through the photographs.

DIEGO: I ate on the plane, thanks.

Marianne stops moving about and tries to draw Diego's attention.

But he is caught up in the mechanisms of his lie. This perpetual lie about his life that other people—even Marianne's closest friends—aren't supposed to know. He goes on, caught up in the mechanism of the lie.

The weather was lovely. The fountains are still there.

There is an element of truth in this lie: a truth for Marianne, like a message. But the lie which conceals this truth provokes an expression of surprise in the others present. In Marianne, it causes embarrassment.

AGNES: The fountains?

Janine turns to her, with an impatient toss of her head. Bill remains impassive. Diego looks at Agnes, who is staring fixedly at him.

DIEGO: The fountains.
AGNES: What fountains?

The tension has become evident.

Automatically, Diego takes a drink from Marianne's hand, without looking at her. He is still facing Agnes.

DIEGO: The fountains of La Piazza Navona, the fountains of Pincio, all the fountains. Don't you know Rome?

There is a note of impatience in his voice.

Marianne turns away. Janine and Bill move closer together.

AGNES: Rome? Oh yes, of course.

Then, in spite of his distance from all this, Diego realizes the embarrassment that has crept into the conversation, and how thick it presently is. But there's nothing he can do about it.

What took you to Rome?

Diego glances at her again and feels like asking her what business it is of hers. But he restrains himself and answers her anyway.

DIEGO: My work. Weren't you aware that I work upon occasion?

He realizes perhaps that he has gone too far, and tries to make amends.

There was a conference sponsored by UNESCO held in Rome, on teaching in undeveloped countries.

Then there is a brief, but heavy silence. As though each of them needed a brief moment to assimilate this news Diego has just given.

JANINE: Aren't you fed up with being an interpreter?

She has spoken in order to break the silence. But Bill looks at her.

Diego's fed up with this situation where he's getting in deeper and deeper. He becomes more caustic.

DIEGO: It pays well. There are no taxes. You work six months a year.

His laugh is almost aggressive.

I don't have any ambitions.

Agnes is still staring at him, as though fascinated.

JANINE: It's getting late. It's time we left you two alone.

Marianne straightens up, her eyes shining.

MARIANNE: You're right, it's terribly late.

There is silence among them, embarrassment. Everyone is standing. Diego too, his glass in his hand.

They are in the foyer. Janine and Bill are putting on their raincoats, gathering their things. Marianne is next to the door, as though she wanted them to leave as soon as possible. Agnes is still making no move to leave.

Diego comes into the foyer, carrying his glass.

In the silence accompanying all these unimportant preparations for departure, Bill says matter of factly, for no apparent reason:

BILL: It looks as though something's developing in Spain.

Diego looks at him. He has no desire to talk about Spain.

DIEGO: Yes, it does.

Maybe that's not enough. He tries to extricate himself by a joke.

As Marianne says: things happen, and happen again, but nothing ever changes.

He forces a laugh. Bill doesn't laugh.
Marianne makes a gesture, a movement, as if she wanted to disclaim any ownership of such a remark.

BILL: And what do you say?
DIEGO: I say nothing.

Bill looks at him: he's hurt. He says something unexpected.

BILL: I'm your friend, Diego.

Then Diego downs the rest of his drink in one gulp.

DIEGO: What I have to say about Spain would offend everyone.

He raises the glass to his lips again, forgetting it is empty.

I'm not even sure it doesn't offend me.

One has the impression that through these words a certain communication has been re-established between Bill and Diego. At least Bill has that impression.

Diego is standing there, his empty glass in his hand. He speaks in a controlled tone of voice, as though he were thinking out loud. He is not speaking to Bill, but rather to the luminous phantoms of Andrés, Roberto, Ramon, and Juan: his own phantoms.

Poor unhappy Spain, heroic Spain, I've had enough of Spain: more than enough. Spain's become the lyrical rallying point of the entire left, a myth for veterans of past wars. Meanwhile, fourteen million tourists go to Spain every year on vacation. All Spain is any more is a tourist's dream, or the myth of the civil war. All of which is mixed up with the theater of Lorca, and I've also had my fill of Lorca's theater: sterile women and rural dramas, who needs them! And that goes for the myth of the civil war too! I never fought at Verdun, and I wasn't at Teruel either, or at the front at Ebro. And the people who are doing things in Spain today, really important things, weren't there either. They're twenty years old, and it's not our past that makes them militant, it's their own future. Spain isn't the dream of '36

any longer, but the truth of '68, however disturbing that may be. More than thirty years have gone by, and the veterans of past wars give me a pain you know where.

They are there, crowded in the entranceway of the apartment. They have no idea why Diego has made this little speech, but a certain portion of what he said made sense to them.

There is again a silence, but this one has another quality.

Diego is staring at his glass, as though asking himself what made him speak.

I'm sorry. All that's not very clear. . . .

He takes a step or two, his empty glass in his hand. He speaks to Bill.

Are you working tomorrow? I'll see you tomorrow.

Bill looks at him and smiles.

BILL: Right. See you tomorrow.

Diego turns to Agnes.

DIEGO: Good night.
AGNES: I'm not going yet.
DIEGO: You're not?

Again, there is a discernible note of irritation in his voice.

AGNES: I have to help Marianne arrange the photographs in order.

She laughs, why nobody knows.

MARIANNE: And then I have to drive her home. She lives in Saint-Cloud, and there are no more trains at this hour.

Diego shrugs his shoulders, almost imperceptibly.

DIEGO: Well, good night anyway.

He turns, looking for a place to set down his glass.
He leaves, picking up his handbag as he goes.
He leaves in silence. Another kind of silence, in which em-

barrassment is no longer the predominant quality. Perhaps perplexity, mingled with a certain concern.

*

He is at the end of a hallway, in front of a door. He has opened this door, turned on the lights, walked into the bedroom, tossed his bag on the bed. He turns and looks around. He looks at everything, deliberately: the objects, the furniture, the lamps which give off a calm, diffused light.

At last, a livable world.

At last!

He's all alone, and has spoken out loud. He takes off his jacket and goes over and sits down on the bed. He lies down, he sees the lights and shadows on the ceiling. The luminous circles, surrounded by larger circles of shadow, on the ceiling.

The door opens. Marianne comes in. She drops onto her knees, on the rug beside the bed. He straightens up and looks at her.

What did that little bitch want, with all those questions?

The obstinate scowl on his face spells trouble.

MARIANNE: You mentioned Rome, and UNESCO. Only ten minutes before that I had said that you were at Geneva for the United Nations.

He wipes his face with his hand.

DIEGO: So they'll think I'm a liar. That's tough.

MARIANNE: You: Why only you? If you've lied, then so have I. It's our whole life that seems like a lie. Didn't you hear Agnes? A phony couple, with a phony life: maybe that's what it seems like.

DIEGO: But it isn't true.

MARIANNE: No, for me it wasn't a lie. You mentioned fountains to me, and I was happy.

She has her head on Diego's knees. She puts her arms around his body.

DIEGO: At this time of night the Piazza Navona is deserted. You can hear the sound of the water.

They are together, lost in the tangible reality of the memory they share. Marianne sits up and looks at him. She stands up and moves away from the bed.

Were are you going?
MARIANNE: Agnes. I have to drive her home.
DIEGO: Can't the little bitch take a taxi?
MARIANNE: Right now she's broke. I promised. It's a long way, she lives in Saint-Cloud.

She steps back toward him and they embrace, a real embrace. They move away from each other. She looks at him.

I wonder whether it wouldn't be better to tell the truth.
DIEGO: Sure. How about an ad in the paper?
MARIANNE: But Diego, we could tell people like Janine and Bill anything.
DIEGO: And what about your friend Agnes, can she be told everything?
MARIANNE: Don't you think they suspect the truth, the way you went on to them a little while ago?
DIEGO: No, Bill doesn't suspect a thing. He's a photographer, he does his job. Anyway, we can never say anything to anyone. It's a question of principle.

She looks at him tenderly.

MARIANNE: Your principles frighten me sometimes.

She is standing again, moving toward the door.
But he doesn't want to appear as though he's giving in, making concessions.

DIEGO: There have been raids in Madrid. A lot of guys have been arrested.

He reminds her of the reasons behind those principles that frighten her sometimes. Again she changes her mind about leaving; she comes back to him and buries herself in his arms.

MARIANNE: And you're leaving? Why are you leaving?

DIEGO: I'm not going to Madrid, I'm going to Barcelona. Everything's quiet in Barcelona.

She looks at him, and there are tears in her eyes.

MARIANNE: I want you to give me a child.

He stops in his tracks, looks at her. Taken completely aback.

As she spoke, her voice was clear, trembling, luminous, desperate.

The way it is now is no life.

DIEGO: Tell me what is?

His voice was hollow.

MARIANNE: A child by you, do you know what that means? My own child by you?

He is bending over her, caressing her back and shoulders. She is trembling.

DIEGO: Listen, let's discuss it again, coolly and calmly.

He has opted for a masculine refuge: the postponement until later, until it can be discussed calmly and rationally, of a problem which disturbs the arrangement, however imperfect, of the status quo.

But she gets to her feet, looks at him, gives a brief, but strangely happy laugh.

MARIANNE: My child: there's no way of talking about it calmly. Afterward you can go away, leave me, forget me if you want to.

She laughs.

DIEGO: It's hardly the right moment.
MARIANNE: Of course it's the right moment.

She is near the door, her hand on the doorknob.
She takes two steps back toward Diego.

Those raids, when did they start?
DIEGO: Three days ago. Last Thursday.
MARIANNE: What is it you want when such things happen?
DIEGO: Want? What do you mean "want"?
MARIANNE: Do you want to carry on, keep on doing what you're doing, even if you're all alone?
DIEGO: But we never are alone. It's important that they know we exist, that the work is still being carried on.
MARIANNE: Yes, I know.

Marianne is at the door to the room, and she opens it. From the other end of the apartment, from the large living room, the sound of music can be heard.

I'll be back.

She gave him a smile, she opened the door wide, left the room and closed the door behind her.
We hear voices outside.

MARIANNE'S VOICE: Agnes! I'm ready to take you!

Diego's face, pensive.

*

Diego is standing, leaning against a bookcase in the bedroom, leafing through some of the books. First he glances at the titles (books published recently, while he was in Spain), then he takes certain ones down from the shelves and leafs through them.

Finally, after some hesitation, he puts aside a few, those he is interested in having beside him tonight, those he wants to open, glance at, perhaps even cut their pages and begin to read.

He takes all these books and tosses them on the bed, where they are strewn.

He sits down on the bed and systematically begins to empty the pockets of his trousers and jacket.

Here, alone, he is going to punctuate certain of his gestures by words or phrases spoken out loud, as though he wanted to establish a certain order out of the chaos of his mind, a certain systematic purpose, in spite of his fatigue.

On the bed, he meticulously arranges the various objects he removes from his pockets into two distinctly different piles.

DIEGO: Bueno, esto por aqui.

He is alone, automatically he talks to himself in Spanish. He tells himself which object must go in which pile.

On one side he puts a number of ordinary objects—a key ring, a pair of metal nail clippers, his wallet (after having carefully examined it and taken certain papers from it, which he puts on the second pile). . . .

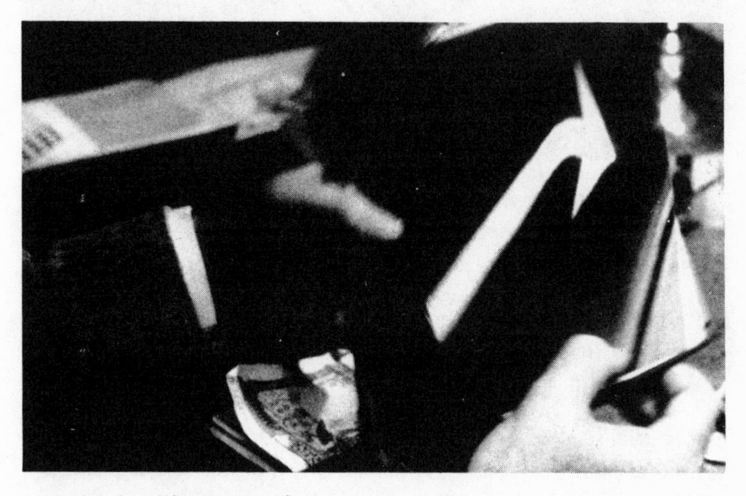

Y lo de allà, por aqui.

On the other side he puts his false French passport. He opens it, looks at the photograph, gets up, goes over to a table, takes a pair of scissors from it, and comes back to the bed.

Ahora, la foto, quitar la foto.

He begins to cut his photograph from the passport, making

sure not to touch the metal clasps which fasten it to the passport, so that a tiny halo of photographic paper, which is of no significance and impossible to identify, remains around each clasp.

He accomplishes this task carefully and slowly, but his mind is elsewhere. That is, he is staring into space.

He burns the remains of his passport photo in an ashtray. He watches the tiny flame consume the paper, and remembers, instantaneously, the fragment of a line of poetry. He gestures broadly, as though he were reciting before a large crowd.

And on the balcony at eventide
Veiled with rosy mists . . .

On the second pile he puts his passport, the papers he has removed from his wallet, and some French and Spanish money.

He gathers together the notes, and the change.

Las cuentas, claro.

He gets up, goes and finds two envelopes.

He puts the Spanish money in one of the envelopes, on which he notes certain figures.

Cena en Madrid: 230. Gasolina: 635. Desayuno: 42.

He puts the French money in the second envelope, after having similarly inscribed certain figures on it. In doing so, he must have thought of Jude, of Jude's wife.

A lucky star, Madam, a very special lucky star only for me, a starfish for every purpose. . . .

He has put away this money which does not belong to him, and which he must account for.

He also puts in the second pile one or two packages of Spanish cigarettes.

Then he goes to take a black leather toilet kit from his bag, which he takes with him into the bathroom. In the bathroom he sets the toilet kit down and removes a tube of toothpaste from it. He opens it on the washbasin. That is, he doesn't unscrew the top, but rather removes the bottom, the part which is normally soldered and which here is half rolled up, the way a half-used tube of toothpaste might be. Then he presses the top part of the tube. The toothpaste squirts out the bottom, and with it a tiny piece of paper rolled up.

He washes this tiny roll of paper under the faucet and rubs the toothpaste on the washbasin, directing the stream of water on it in order to dissolve it. After washing the roll of paper, he dries it on the towel.

He comes back into the bedroom.

Beneath the light of a lamp, he unties the rubber band around the tiny roll. Then he unfolds several layers of cellophane, inside of which there are two or three sheets of onionskin paper, which he carefully lays flat on a straight surface, flattening them with the palm of his hand. He looks at the sheets, which are covered with tiny handwriting, then puts them in his wallet.

When he has finished sorting all these objects, he goes to the far end of the room. There he opens a piece of furniture —a kind of chest—inisde which is an Electrophone. He takes out the Electophone and sets it down somewhere. With a letter opener he unscrews the bottom of the chest, exposing an empty area beneath. From it he takes out an envelope containing his real identity papers: a French identity card, driver's license . . .

He is going to put these real papers in his wallet, and everything else he has prepared in the false bottom of the chest.

He has second thoughts and takes back his French passport —that is, René Sallanches' passport—which he puts away in his coat pocket, after having wrapped it in paper and sealed it with scotch tape.

He screws the bottom of the chest back into place and rearranges everything so that it looks exactly as before.

He is standing in the middle of the room. He lights a cigarette.

But patience and irony are the principal virtues of the Bolsheviks.

He seems to be reciting, as he had been a while before. One would think it was a verse by Mayakovski, but it was not, however similar sounding it was.

He has spoken in a loud, emphatic voice.

He walks toward the bed.

My name is Nana.

He stretches out on the bed, among the books he has chosen.

And my name's Domingo.

He closes his eyes; he is still smoking a cigarette.
Almost immediately, he gets up, as though he had forgotten something. He goes out of the room, walks down the hallway, and cautiously opens a door.

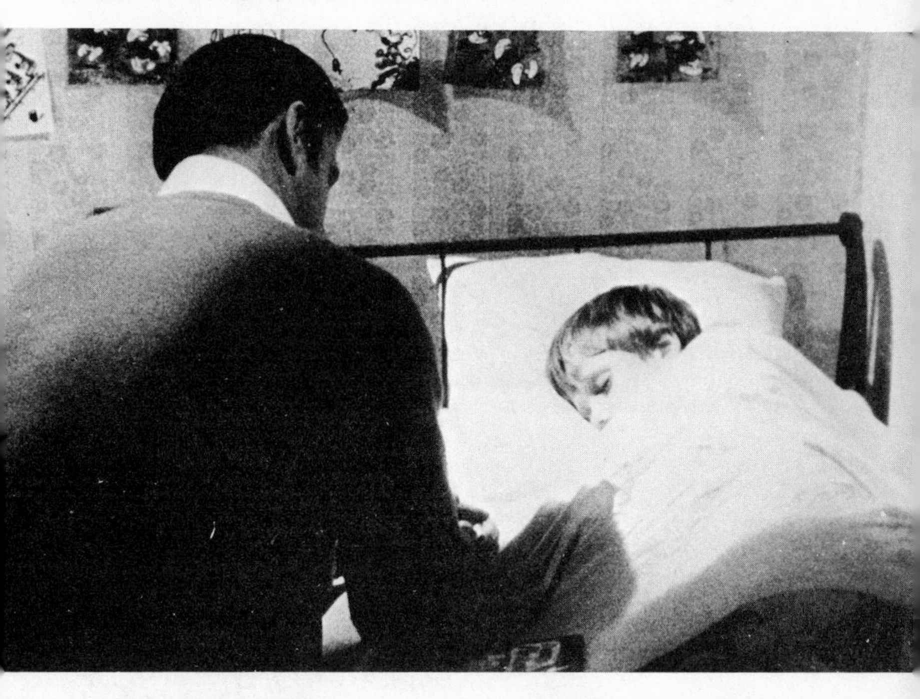

A twelve-year-old boy is asleep in bed. Diego looks at him: it is Patrick, Marianne's son from a marriage that ended in divorce. Diego walks over to a blackboard on which are written various messages from Marianne to her son, and from him to his mother. Some of them are half-erased. Diego takes a piece of chalk and writes something for Patrick. Again he looks at him sleeping, then goes out, after having turned off the light.
He is back in his room, lying on the bed. Perhaps, with his eyes closed, is he imagining Marianne's return, picturing how

they will make love. Or perhaps he has actually fallen asleep, and he is dreaming that they are making love. Or perhaps the shots are not out of dreams or daydreams at all: perhaps they are really there, in their room, making love. Or have just made love.

The room is different, the light having changed. Through the open window, from behind the drawn curtains, can be heard the light patter of a spring rain on the trees along the quai de Bethune, on the roofs, on the Seine.

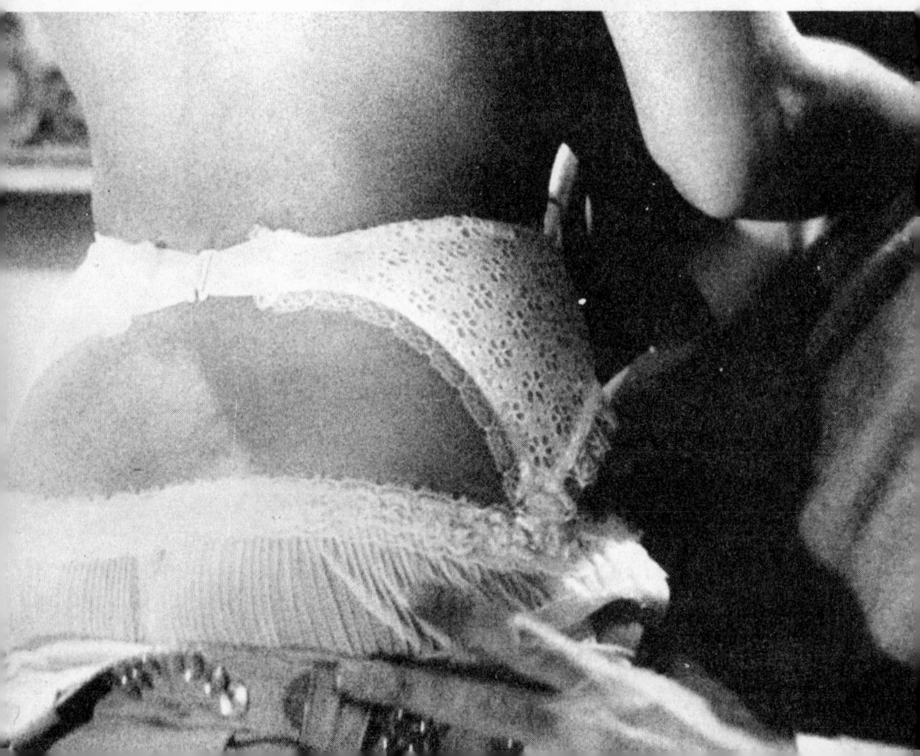

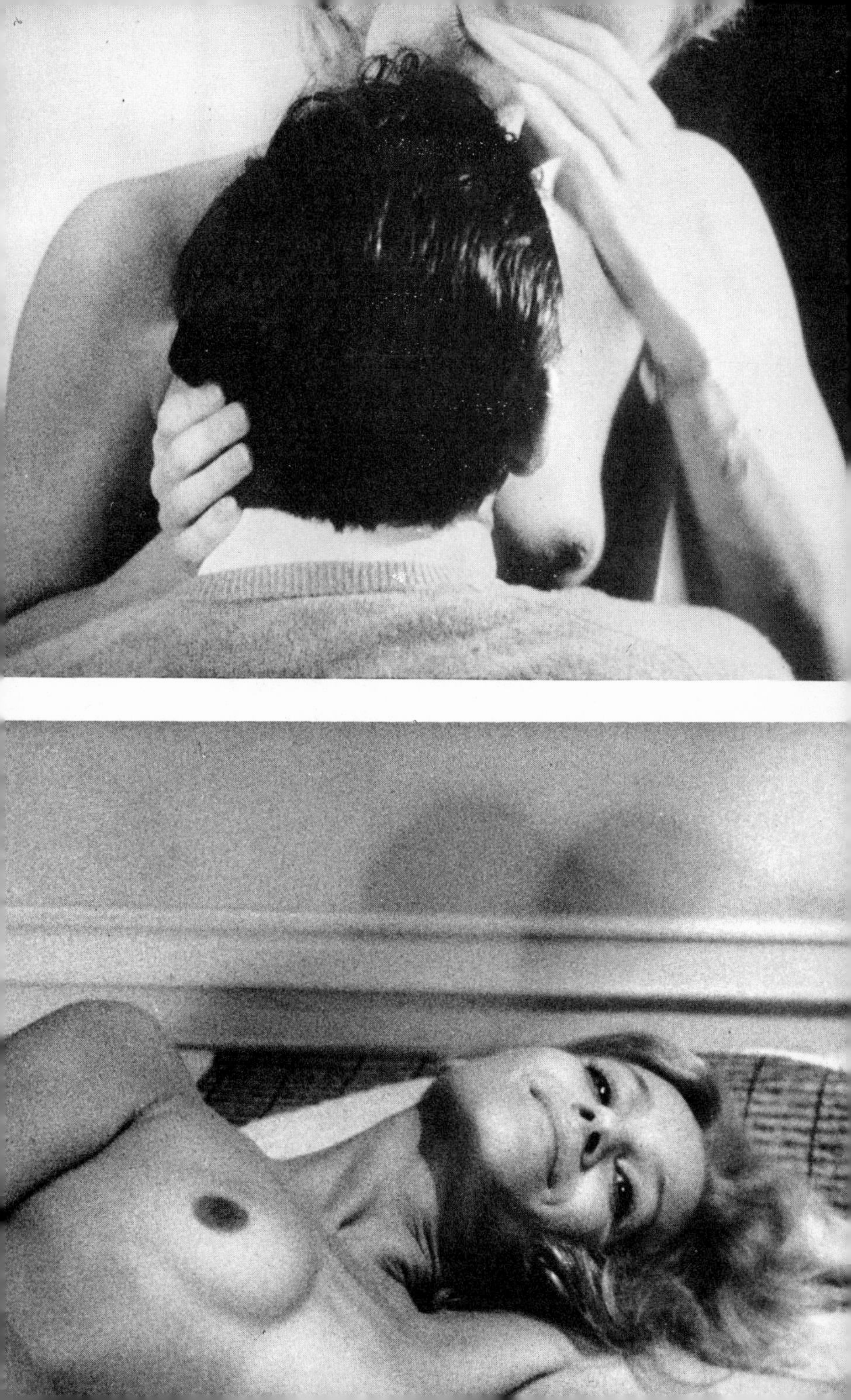

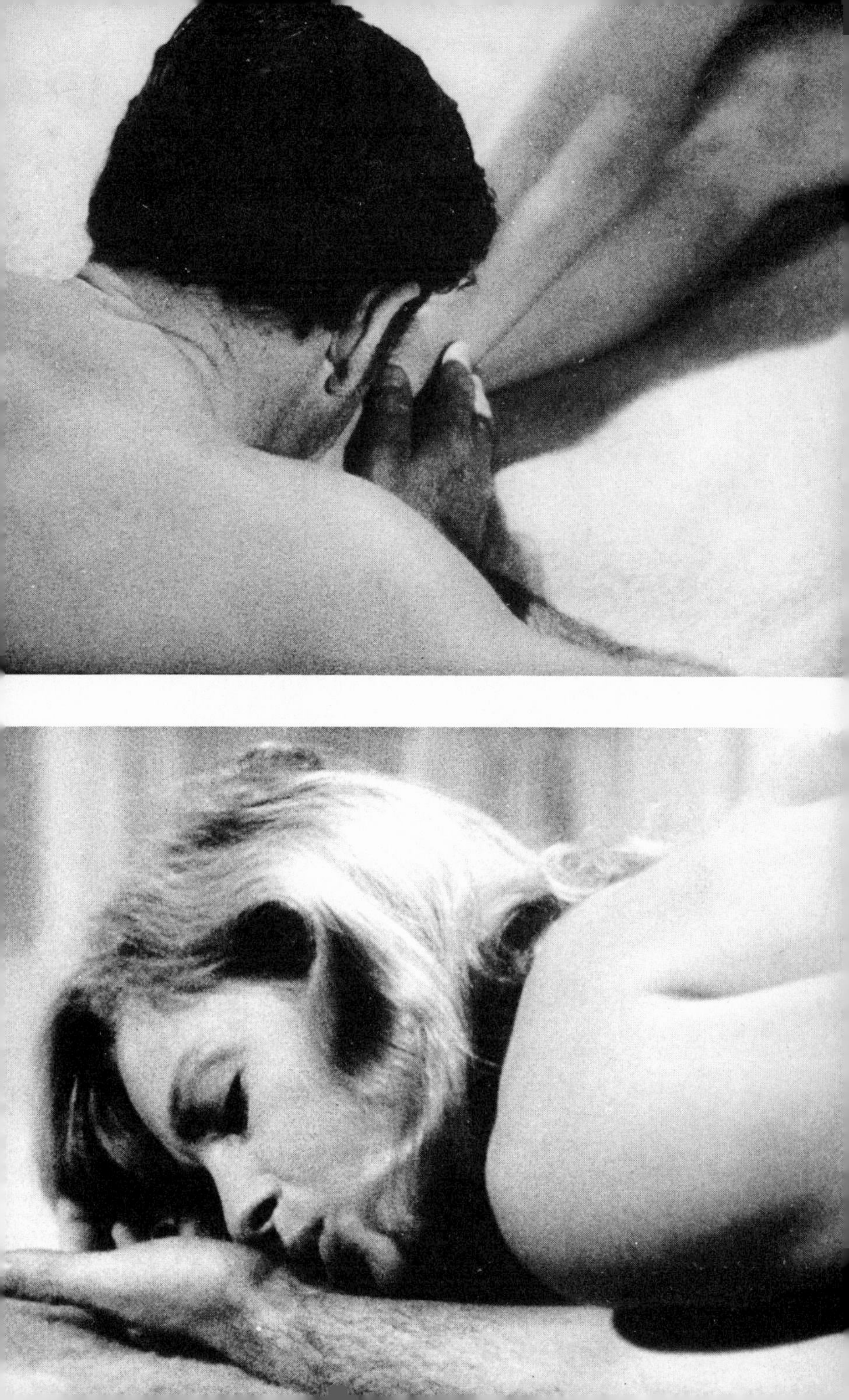

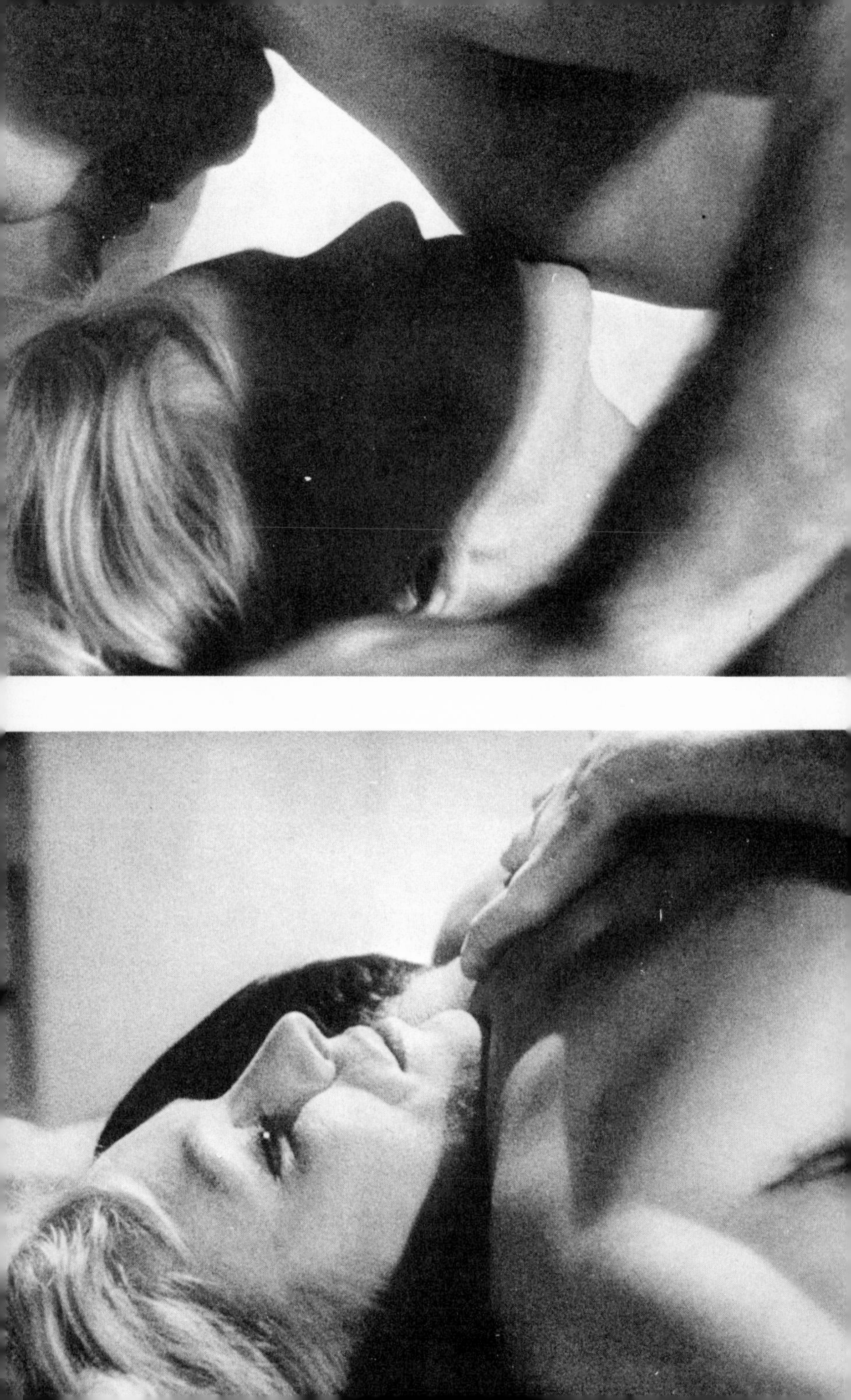

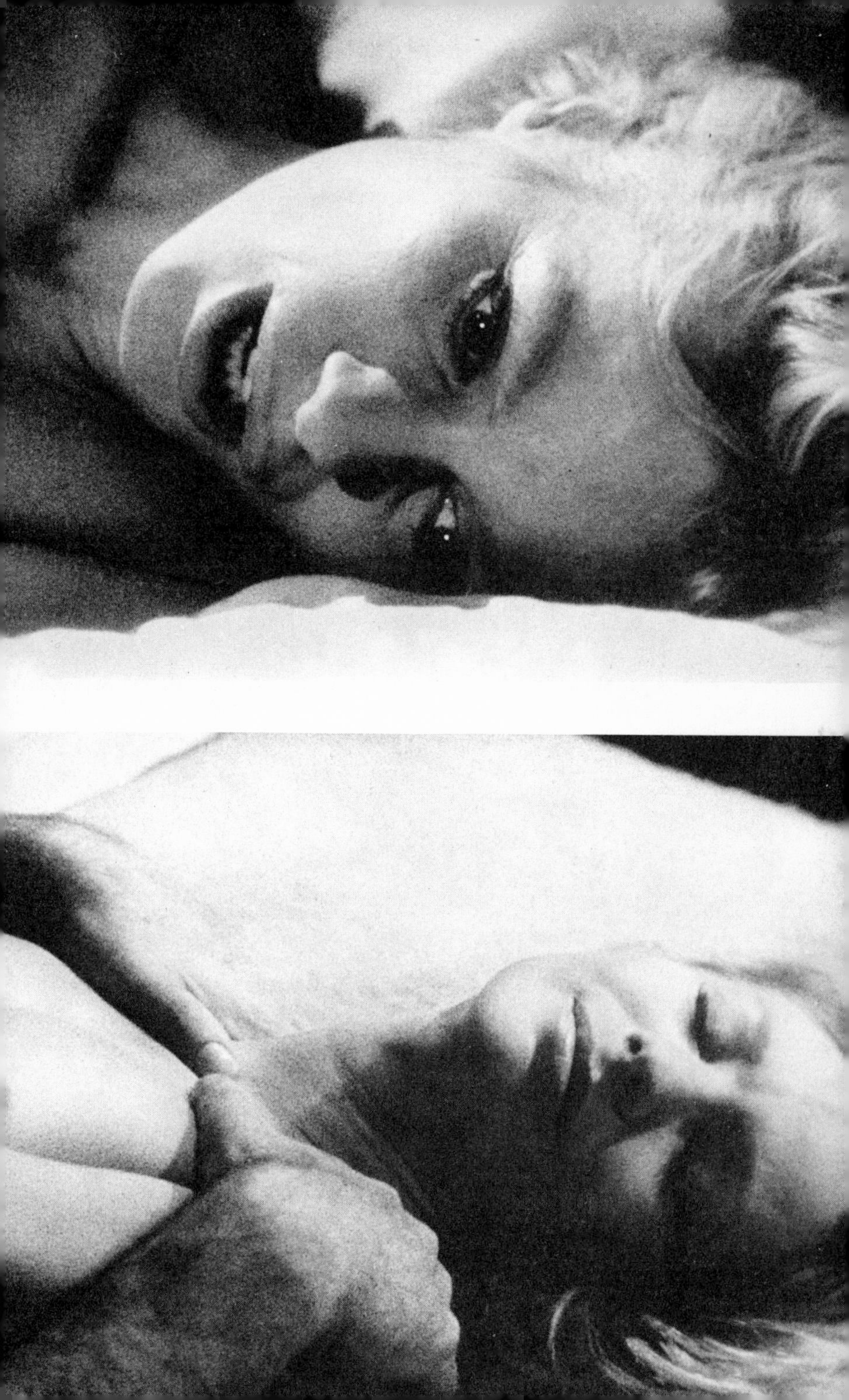

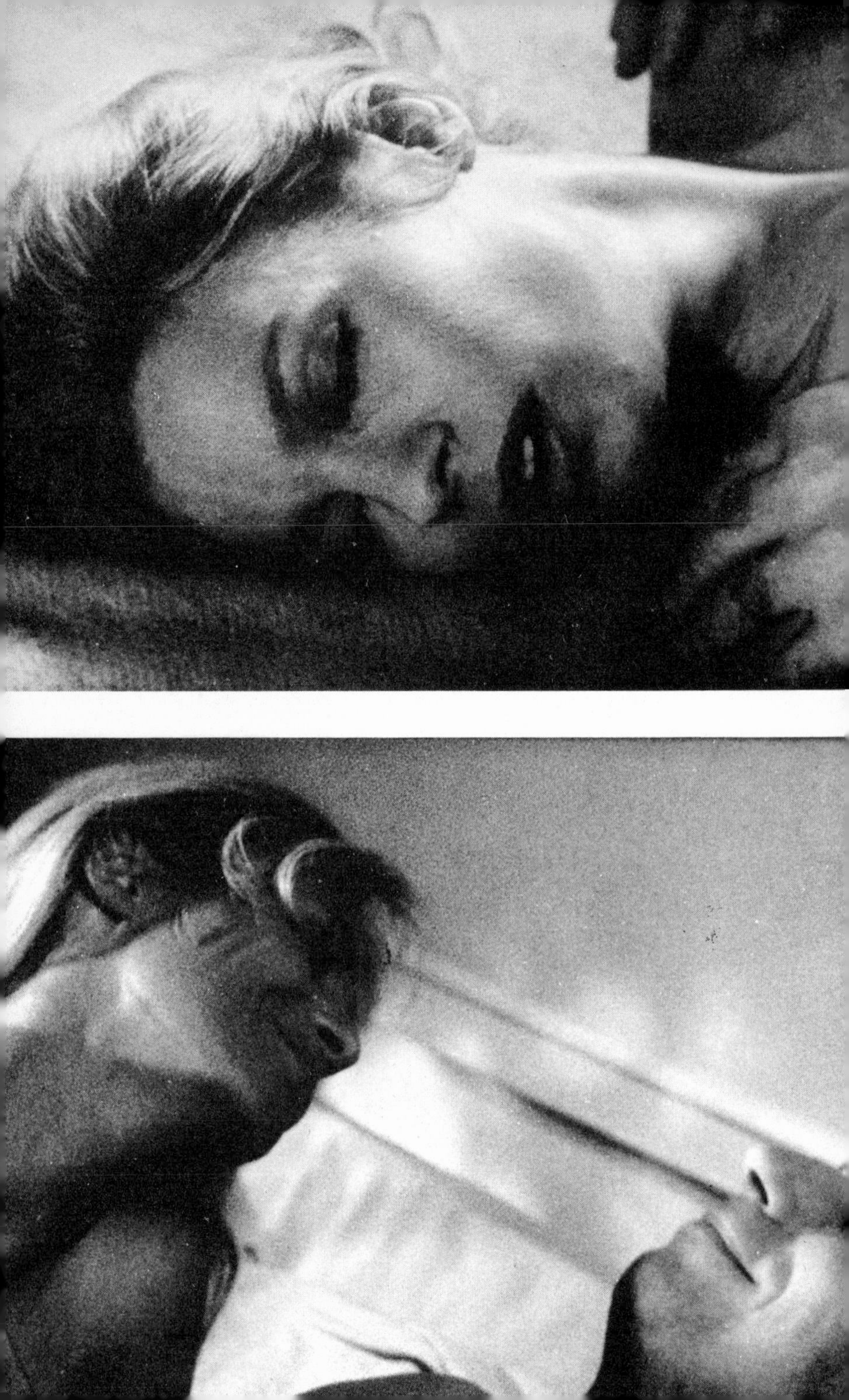

Marianne is in bed, naked, beneath the sheet, her bare shoulders visible. Alone in bed, her face lighted, speaking to Diego, who is invisible, who is watching her.

Or speaking to herself.

MARRIANNE: Six months without seeing you, Diego, it's an impossible situation. . . . If you had to stop what you're doing, if you had to stay here . . . I don't know . . . if things became too dangerous for you to go to Madrid . . . would you miss it?

DIEGO'S VOICE: I would miss Spain, yes I would. Like something you really miss, truly and deeply, whose absence becomes unbearable. . . . Your friends . . . The unknown people who open a door when you knock and who recognize you, as you recognize them. You're part and parcel of something.

MARIANNE: Spain, your friends: that's your life.

There is a brief silence.

MARIANNE: The other day I almost went to bed with a man.

DIEGO'S VOICE: Why?

MARIANNE: Because I thought I wanted to.

DIEGO: But you didn't want to. Why are you telling me about it?

MARIANNE: Would you tell, Diego?

He has come over close to her, on the bed. There is a silence.

DIEGO: I don't know.

A further silence. She is looking at him.

I don't know.

She has got out of bed. Diego is alone, sitting, or rather lying down. He has lighted a cigarette.

Why didn't you do it?

After a brief silence, in the semidarkness of the room, Marianne's Voice can be heard over the sound of the rain.

And the room, in the semidarkness, with the sound of the rain in the background, begins to live, to take on a life of its own as Marianne speaks, each piece of furniture, each object becoming more clearly defined, gleaming in the semidarkness.

The room is inhabited too by Diego's face, which is present there, which is perhaps the remembrance of Diego's face, as though Marianne were speaking to all these remembered Diegos.

MARIANNE'S VOICE: Because there always comes a time when it's no longer possible, when one can no longer go to bed with a man, make love with him. . . .

A short silence, over the objects in the room, over Diego's face.

Or else he has to be gone, to have disappeared. But to wake up beside someone other than you, Diego, is inconceivable.

Another short silence.

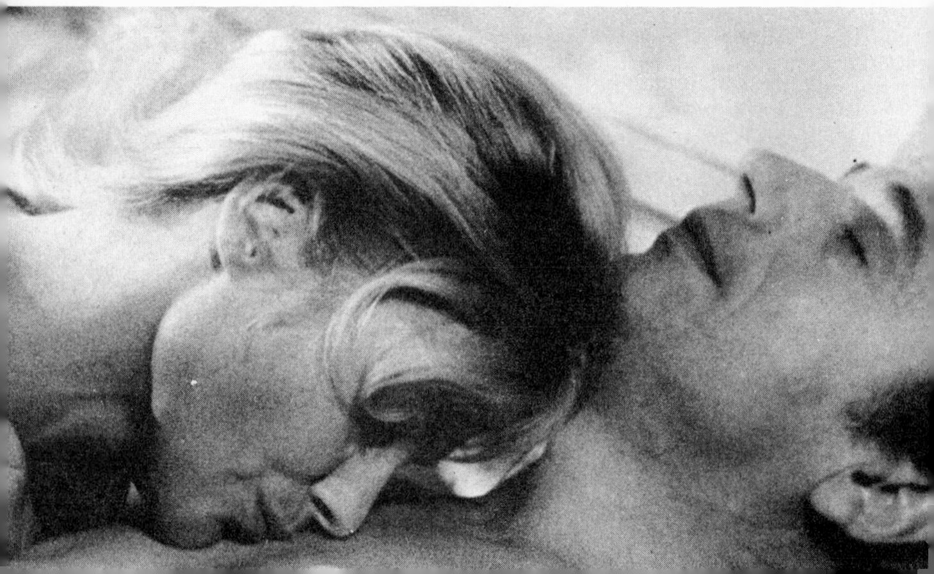

It's afterward that the complications set in. Don't you agree?

Diego has stirred. He straightens up.

DIEGO: I'm hungry.

Once again Marianne is visible.

MARIANNE: I thought you ate dinner on the plane, on your way from Rome.

This brings them back to Diego's lie of a while back. To the truth that this lie concealed. A lie only the two of them are privy to, and they both laugh. They are in each other's arms.

Nine years ago, I was the one you lied to. In that restaurant on the Piazza Navona, all you could think of was one thing: I mustn't know who you were, or what you were doing in Rome.

DIEGO: Of course.

MARIANNE: You told me your name was Francisco, and then you said it was Rafael, and then Carlos. It took me months, both in Rome and later in Paris, to ferret out your truth from among your lies.

DIEGO: They weren't lies, they were obstacles.

MARIANNE: Why?

DIEGO: Falling in love is not provided for in the life of a professional revolutionary.

MARIANNE: What is?

He reflects for a moment.

DIEGO: Patience. Above all, patience.

She looks at him.

Listen, I'm famished. Don't you have anything to eat?

His voice has betrayed a note of impatience. They both are aware of the fact, and burst out laughing.

*

A table covered with plates of cold cuts, pickles, cold roast chicken, and fresh bread. A bottle of red Bordeaux. A typical midnight snack, especially enjoyable at 2:00 A.M., *and Diego is eating with obvious relish. They are in the kitchen. Marianne watches Diego as he eats. She is smoking a king-sized filter cigarette.*

MARIANNE: In October, if you are still leading this same life, I'm moving to Madrid.
DIEGO: Of course I'll still be leading it.

He pauses for a second, as though he were just realizing the decision Marianne had calmly informed him of.

Moving to Madrid? What do you mean, moving?
MARIANNE: Live there, find a job. Move: it's very simple.
DIEGO: To Madrid? But you hardly speak ten words of Spanish.
MARIANNE: I learned French didn't I?
DIEGO: Job? What kind of job?

He seems irritated by Marianne's plans.

MARIANNE: The same kind. They also publish books in Spain don't they?
DIEGO: In any case, you won't be able to live on my eight hundred francs a month.
MARIANNE: I thought you got a raise?
DIEGO: You're right: eight hundred and seventy-five francs a month. How much do you earn here? Three thousand a

month? Listen, you're out of your mind. You'll never find the same setup.

MARIANNE: But I don't need the same setup. I need you.

Diego realizes that he will have to resort to better arguments than those.

DIEGO: Anyhow, it's out of the question: it's contrary to every principle.

MARIANNE: What, again?

DIEGO: A wife, in the same city where you're working clandestinely, means multiplying the risks.

This last was said on a peremptory tone.

MARIANNE: How serious was it this time? Were any of those arrested from among the Paris group?

DIEGO: You know Juan . . .

She breaks in, crying out.

MARIANNE: Was Juan arrested?

DIEGO: Not yet. That's why I came back. But I'm positive they have his photograph and are waiting for him in Madrid.

Night is upon them.

This night which is upon them, in this lightless room, is inhabited by that music that he thought he heard a few hours before when he was walking, along the rue du Cardinal Lemoine, over the pont de Sully, toward this house, this woman, this music.

Night is upon them, with only a faint suggestion of dawn trembling on the edge of night, of gray dawn, of the pale pink of a spring dawn, of the gray-pink of the Seine's freshness, of life beginning again.

In the pink and gray night of the room, Marianne's shadow stirs, enveloped in a long dressing gown. Marianne's shadow, with brief flashes of light which cling fleetingly to her hair, her lips, her eyes, her hands.

Marianne's shadow moves toward the door of the room, while Diego's stirs in bed.

Marianne turns around.

MARIANNE: Diego?

She has spoken softly. Diego does not reply. She leaves the room.

She is in the hallway, walking through her house, which at present, with the gray and pink reflections of dawn, is quite different than it was the night before.

For the first time since the story began, Diego is absent: it is not his eyes, his movements, his actions which give a structure, a psychological reality to the world.

Diego is absent, but it is his invisible presence, his heavy breathing, that dictates Marianne's long, slow walk through her house: Diego's house.

She goes into the kitchen, pours herself a tall glass of mineral water, and walks through her house, the glass in her hand.

She is in the large living room, which she straightened up after her friends had left, which is neat now, vaguely lighted by the gray and pink tints of nascent dawn.

She shivers in the coolness of dawn, next to a window which is wide open.

Around her, as she walks without purpose through her house, in the music of this house the objects begin to live, to

have a meaning, to become charged with affective resonances.

In the midst of all this, is Diego: Diego absent, Diego asleep, Diego in the future, in the past, Diego occupying each parcel of time.

She walks, slowly, picking up an object here and there, looking at it, putting it down in another spot, in Diego's house overlooking the Seine, in the gray and pink light of daybreak in spring.

Finally she comes back to the kitchen, where she begins to make coffee for Diego.

In the music of this gray and pink dawn, calmly, tenderly, she begins her daily routine.

III

Exile Is a Tough Profession

IVRY. 8:30 A.M. Monday, April 19, 1965.

The final shots of Marianne are accompanied by the sound of the Paris subway's rumble, a sound rather divined than actually heard at first—it is only later that we realize that it was the rumble of the Metro we had been hearing.

Now the rumble of the Metro fills the screen while the line of cars arrives and stops at the station. It is the Pierre-Curie stop, the next to last stop on the Mairie d'Ivry–Porte de la Villete–Pré Saint-Gervais line, when the train is heading for Mairie d'Ivry.

Diego steps out onto the platform. Walking quickly, he heads toward the exit, passing the other passengers who had got out of the subway at the same stop. He walks so rapidly he is almost running: he is late.

There are two exits at the Pierre-Curie stop. Diego appears at one of them, looks around. On the opposite side of the street, near the other exit, Roberto is pacing nervously back and forth.

They see each other; Roberto stops pacing.

He has crossed the street; he is next to Roberto.

They are talking, Roberto must be chiding Diego for being late. But it's impossible to tell this exactly from their gestures, which are vague and incomprehensible: it is not a mime show, with one clearly upbraiding the other and the second offering some more or less valid excuse for the delay.

They walk down a street which descends rather sharply and turns. A street reserved for pedestrians only.

They emerge into an open space where, in the midst of the older low-lying dwellings of Ivry, loom—perhaps monstrous by comparison—the squat square blocks of government-subsidized apartment buildings, dominated by their towers.

Diego looks up at the towers, and the Narrator's Voice is heard.

NARRATOR'S VOICE: Ivry, Porte des Lilas, Six-Routes et Quatre-Chemins, Aubervilliers, la Poterne des Peupliers, Victor-Hugo, Juarès, Paul Vaillant-Couturier: you know these suburbs like the back of your hand. You arrive from your own country and, every time you do, you again see this landscape of exile.

They enter one of the buildings and take an elevator.

And you're going to see once again these indefatigable, dessicated, worn-out men, who overlook no detail but have lost perspective of the whole, who are ready to die for their dream: your comrades.

They are in the elevator, saying nothing.

You're going to find once again this irreplaceable fraternity which, none the less, is being eaten away, often by lack of reality: in Ivry, or in Aubervilliers, spending days at a time trying to reconstruct your country, to make it resemble your dreams, to turn your dreams into the far-off reality of Spain by dint of hard, stubborn work.

They have left the elevator, are walking down a hallway, push open a glass-windowed door, turn right into another hallway, reach a door. All without exchanging a word.

This time Roberto rings three times: two short and one long.

The door opens immediately, as though someone had been waiting and watching for them. A woman holds the door open, then moves aside to let them in, greeting them as she does.

THE WOMAN: Hello, comrades!

They return her greeting, walk past her, and are in the living room. The room resembles all the rooms we have seen, all the rooms we will see: a television, cheap modern furniture, cold colors.

A man is at the far end of the room, looking out the wide window. When they come in, he turns around. He smiles at Diego and makes a gesture of welcome. Diego walks toward him, also smiling. They embrace, the way Spanish men do.

The man who was there, who is holding Diego in his arms —and on both their faces emotion is visible, the joy at seeing each other again—is about fifty years old, of medium height, a man of unshifting gaze, soberly dressed in the manner a high government official would dress. He has a line of bitterness around his mouth, but he still knows how to smile, and often does, perhaps somewhat paternally. He is a man convinced of the reasons why he is right, but tolerant of those who betray doubts, uncertainties, and hesitation.

A fully mature man, in the full possession of his faculties, obviously possessed of a stubborn, indomitable will.

He is the Chief, the man in charge.

THE CHIEF: Carlos, como estàs?

He has moved slightly back and is looking at Diego (that is, once again, Carlos). He holds him at arm's length as he asks him how he is.

DIEGO: Bien, muy bien. Y tú?

They both laugh, and embrace again in Spanish fashion.

Another man comes over. Shorter than the Chief, he is bald and wears glasses. He shakes Diego's hand.

MANOLO: Qué tal? Has tenido buen viaje?

They are seated around the table. The Chief is sitting with his back to the window. Diego is opposite him, Roberto is at his left, Manolo at his right.

The Chief opens his briefcase and takes out some white sheets of paper, a thick notebook, and a newspaper.

He places the newspaper before him, folded double, open to an inside page.

THE CHIEF: Ya viene en el periódico.

He then reads, in French, which he pronounces correctly but with an accent, the following excerpt. As he reads, the faces around the table are attentive but impassive.

> "According to reports received from official sources, the Spanish police have apparently carried out over the past

few days a vast preventive operation in Madrid against various left-wing groups of the working class. A printing plant is reported to have been discovered, and several dozen arrests made, including the arrest of several leaders who had entered Spain illegally. It appears that this operation is directly linked to the unrest which has occurred during the past few months among the working classes of the Spanish capital."

He has finished reading, his face betrays no emotion, he puts the newspaper back into his briefcase.

Silence.

The Chief calmly lights a cigarette. Just then, the woman who had opened the door for Diego and Roberto comes in carrying a tray: cups of coffee, a coffee pot, and a sugar bowl.

THE WOMAN: Coffee's ready. I know you all take it.

They clean off a section of the table to make room for the tray.

THE CHIEF: What a good idea!

He has an affable smile as he looks at the woman put the tray down on the table.

THE WOMAN: I'm going to run a few errands. If anyone rings, don't open the door.

The Chief and the man with glasses on his right nod in reply to her admonition.

Again they are alone, stirring their coffee.

Then Diego takes from his wallet the papers he has brought back with him to France concealed in the tube of toothpaste. He unfolds the papers in front of him, repeating his gestures of the previous evening.

The Chief calmly watches them all.

THE CHIEF: Bueno, podemos empezar.

He gestures to Diego, as though to give him the floor. Diego looks at his papers and begins to speak.

DIEGO: Voy a intentar resumir la situación, camaradas, segun las noticías que teníamos el sábado.

He tells them that he is going to try and bring them up to date on the situation so far as he knows it through the latest news of the preceding Saturday.

As he speaks, Diego's face occupies the entire screen. Then, after he has lighted a cigarette and glanced again at his papers, it disappears altogether.

Impassive, the Chief takes notes. Roberto is listening: he also has some paper in front of him, but he is not taking notes. Manolo is also listening, while glancing at some papers he has in front of him on the table.

Meanwhile, the Narrator's Voice is heard.

NARRATOR'S VOICE: You have a feeling you've already lived through this experience before, you're saying words you've already spoken over the years. How many times have you already come in the past, after a wave of arrests, after a "fall." In Spanish we call it a "fall": we say that this or that buddy has "fallen," that a printing plant, or an organization, has "fallen." Sooner or later, the veterans say, you fall. Everyone falls. It's a long march punctuated with falls. How many times have you returned, to explain why these falls occurred, and to decide what measures had to be taken. . . .

A poorly extinguished cigarette butt lies smoking in the ashtray. Manolo leans forward to snuff it out completely.

Andrés failed to show up for his appointment at the Botanical Gardens: that's when it all began, Thursday evening. Three days ago.

Diego's face reappears on the screen.

DIEGO: El viernes estuvo claro que habia caído la imprenta. Luego llegaron noticias de Pegaso.

He breaks off. His gaze encompasses this room, the faces before him, but without his really seeing them. He is elsewhere, in Madrid, with the friends who have fallen.

*

Time has passed. The ashtray is filled with butts. Roberto is coming back from the window, which he has opened a crack because of the smoke.

Diego has finished speaking. Roberto is seated again. He looks at the notes he has taken.

The Chief turns to Roberto, then to Manolo, his eyes asking each in turn whether he has anything to say, whether he has an opinion to express. Both of them remain impassive, however. Perhaps they have nothing to add, or—and this is more likely —perhaps they are waiting for the Chief to give his opinion: in any case, they will agree with what he says.

Then the Chief arranges his notes in front of him. He glances at them, preparing to speak.

THE CHIEF: Carlos nos ha presantado un cuadro de la situación, totalmente subjectivo. Exagera las consecuencias de la caída, yo diria que hasta parece haber perdido toda perspectiva política.

He has started right in, his loud solemn voice emphasizing certain words. His face, seen in a close-up as he begins to speak, is the epitome of confidence, expressing self-assurance and resolution.

Then his face disappears from the screen. All the rest of his speech will be voice-over the faces of the three others.

Diego's face, bearing the brunt of the attack, remains impassive. And yet at times there is an expression of surprise visible in his eyes. And at times, too, there is an unconscious nervous twitch of the eyebrows which destroys the seeming impassiveness of Diego's face.

The two other faces look solemn. At times they react to the Chief's strong words by signs of approval.

The rest of his remarks, except for the few moments when he pauses to check his notes or catch his breath, in which cases his face will appear again on the screen, will be spoken in English. But it will not be he who is speaking, with his heavily accented voice of a short while back as he read the newspaper dispatch. There is no need for realism. It will be an English voice, strong, clear, and clipped, which will speak the rest of his speech.

THE CHIEF'S VOICE: Carlos has given us a completely subjective appraisal of the situation. He exaggerates the consequences of the arrests presently being made. I might even go so far as to say that he seems to have lost all political perspective.

The faces of Roberto and the man with glasses: solemn.

Diego's face, perplexed, but frozen. He sits up straighter in his chair.

What is the situation that has led to these arrests? It is a situation which finds the working class, the students, and the peasants taking the offensive. A situation in which the dictatorship is filled with panic, harried to death.

The face of the Chief, who pauses for a moment to look at his notes.

Even the police measures currently being carried out reflect this fear on the part of the regime in face of the rising tide of resistance by the masses. Under these conditions, the regime cannot prevent this movement from advancing and growing.

The faces of Roberto and the man with glasses, more and more solemn, clearly showing their approval of the Chief's words.

Diego's face is attentive.

We are in a prerevolutionary situation, we are moving toward a general political strike.

The Chief's face, as he pauses once more.

This is why we sent Juan to Madrid with precise orders and instructions. This movement of the masses needs to be organized and unified, its goal clearly defined. And that goal is a general strike. Conditions for such a strike are now favorable, we must strike while the time is right. Dates must be set, and this we have already done.

Diego's face evinces surprise. His entire body has moved at this news.

Roberto and Manolo are looking at him. Their faces express a full range of feelings: satisfaction, unshakable confidence, rightful indignation with respect to Diego, who does not seem to agree.

The general strike has been set for April 30th.

Shots of Diego's face—he is hanging on the Chief's every word—and of Roberto's and Manolo's.

And on May 1st there will be demonstrations in every city in Spain.

Diego's face, which turns to Manolo and Roberto, as though he were thunderstruck. Manolo hands him some papers—newspapers, tracts, etc.—which Diego examines.

Carlos disagrees with the decision to call a general strike. He says we must take into account the realities of the situation. Fine. But what does this really mean? That we should allow the political situation to evolve by itself until it is ripe? That would be mere opportunism, purely and simply. . . .

Diego raises his eyes from the papers he is reading.

DIEGO: Nunca he dicho eso: que nos dejemos llevar por la espontaneidad.

Now the Narrator's Voice will break in again, to comment on Diego's thoughts.

NARRATOR'S VOICE: You never said that: that we ought to give ourselves up to spontaneity. You are merely questioning certain kinds of action in certain circumstances. A general strike isn't the only form of struggle, the inevitable conclusion of partial movements. Lenin has already formulated certain criticisms of the general strike insofar as it tends to preclude other forms of struggle.

Shots of the faces of the three others while the Narrator's Voice reveals Diego's thoughts.

But the Chief is going to begin speaking again. His face is visible as he starts to speak in Spanish, but the camera leaves his face as the voice-over in English breaks in, to explore the room, the objects, the faces of Roberto, Manolo, and Diego.

THE CHIEF'S VOICE: If you want to bring Lenin into the conversation, then let's do so. You accuse us of narrow-mindedness, but if you'll recall, Lenin in fact proved that a dose of narrow-mindedness, of revolutionary subjectivism, is indispensable. Your criticism is purely negative. What are you actually proposing?

His words are addressed directly to Diego, and it is Diego who will reply to him.

DIEGO: La critica siempre es negativa, en un primer momento.

The Narrator's Voice continues the reply, as the camera leaves Diego's face.

NARRATOR'S VOICE: You're trying to make yourself understood, trying to explain that it's not the idea of a general strike that you're criticizing but simply the actual conditions under which it is being applied. You're saying that calling a strike for April 30th is out of the question because the required conditions are lacking. And another failure might risk alienating the masses from this form of action. You also say that it is impossible to set a date and decide the kind of action that is to take place inside Spain from a post in exile. We cannot put ourselves in the shoes of the workers in Bilbao, Barcelona, or Madrid, and decide for them. The clandestine underground can only be the organizer, the instrument of the will of the masses. It cannot replace that will.

THE CHIEF'S VOICE: Why do you predicate as opposites exiles and those inside Spain, the underground and the masses?

Diego's face expresses confusion: he is not succeeding in getting his point across.

DIEGO: No los opongo. Digo que lo uno no puede sustituir a lo otro.

Diego says that he is making no such comparison. He is merely saying that one cannot replace the other.

More time has passed. Manolo has emptied the ashtray again and opened the window to air the room. The Chief is speaking again.

THE CHIEF'S VOICE: I don't mean to imply that Carlos has let himself be unduly impressed by the arrests—that would be absurd. He's proved often over the past ten years that he doesn't allow himself to be easily intimidated. But he has shown a lack of political perspicacity. What, in actual fact, is the situation?

Shots of the three men's faces as they await the Chief's verdict.

Juan is in Barcelona. He is supposed to meet Carlos in

Madrid next Thursday. But Carlos is here, leaving Juan abandoned to his own devices. Therefore we have to get in contact with Juan and set up another contact for him with the Madrid organization. We've got to multiply the number of trips, and as a result automatically multiply the risks. That in a nutshell is what Carlos' precipitation has led to.

Shot of the Chief's face after rendering his verdict; he follows it with a moment's silence.

If, on the other hand, Carlos had stayed in Madrid, he could have followed hour by hour the progress of the raid. He could have taken certain steps. Juan would have been protected by the presence of Carlos in Madrid. We see then the consequences of an individual action lightly taken, without taking into account the exigencies of the act and without respecting the decisions made by the central committee.

The accusation is serious. The faces of Roberto and Manolo freeze in an expression of horrified reprobation.

The meeting is over. Manolo is gathering his papers. The Chief has put on his raincoat, he goes over to Diego who is standing stock-still by the window. He speaks to Diego, pats him on the shoulder paternally. Meanwhile, the Narrator's Voice is heard voice-over.

NARRATOR'S VOICE: You're not going to go to Barcelona, you're staying here. It's Ramon who's going to Barcelona, who will accompany Juan to Madrid. You've just spent six months in Spain, caught up in the welter of daily events. Maybe you are blinded by the details of a partial reality, dozens of true little details that cloud your vision, so it seems. You're going to take some rest, you've got to think things over, talk things over with yourself. You're staying here.

*

Diego is alone in the living room. He is watching out the bay window the movements in the street ten or twelve stories below.

Images flit through his mind: Marianne's face, happy and smiling. Images of long walks in the forest with Marianne. Sometimes—rapidly, as though they were immediately erased by an act of self-censorship—the image of Nadine superimposes itself over that of Marianne in Diego's mind.

Roberto comes back into the room, and Diego turns to him.

ROBERTO: Vamos?

Diego remains caught up in his own thoughts, his own preoccupations.

Qué, vamos?

Diego comes over to him.

DIEGO: Hay que ocuparse del pasaporte.

He takes René Sallanches' passport from his pocket.

*

He puts the passport, open, on the table. Open to the page where his photograph is missing, the photo he has carefully cut out the night before.

Shot of the passport, open to the page where the photograph is missing.

Diego is contemplating this page, perhaps without really seeing it, if one is to judge by the expression in his eyes.

Around him, a large room which looks like a painter's studio, with a skylight. A photographer's studio, perhaps, judging by the equipment there.

At the other end of the studio, a man in a long white smock is rummaging in a metal file cabinet.

MAN IN THE WHITE SMOCK: Sallanches . . . Sallanches . . . Sallanches . . .

He pronounces the name out loud, with a Spanish accent, as he rummages in the file.

Roberto is seated near a table located halfway between Diego and the man in the white smock.

Aqui está!

He leaves the file cabinet and comes over toward Diego and Roberto carrying a large envelope of thick brown paper in his hand.

He removes a piece of paper from the envelope, on which a photo is fastened. He reads.

René Sallanches: born April 23, 1921, civil engineer employed by the government. Residence: rue de l'Estrapade . . .

Diego goes over to him, puts out his hand, and looks at the photograph of Nadine's father.

The Man in the White Smock takes the passport, opens it, and places the photo of Nadine's father in the spot where it is supposed to be. He is doing this on the table, and he holds the photograph with his finger as Diego watches.

Es cosa de un minuto.

He takes the passport, and the photo of Nadine's father, and again he moves over toward his work table, which is bathed in a bright light.

ROBERTO: Hace falta un pasaporte para Ramon.

The Man in the White Smock turns around. He looks at Roberto.

THE MAN IN THE WHITE SMOCK: Ramon?

Roberto nods affirmatively.

Cuando?

Roberto has said that Ramon will need a passport, and the other man has asked when he has to have it.

ROBERTO: Hoy.

He will need it today.

THE MAN IN THE WHITE SMOCK: Hoy?
ROBERTO: Esta tarde.

Roberto adds that he will need it no later than this afternoon. The Man in the White Smock shrugs his shoulders in disgust.

THE MAN IN THE WHITE SMOCK: Siempre con prisas, coño!

Why are they always so rushed? But Roberto does not allow himself to be intimidated. He answers calmly.

ROBERTO: Siempre.

Moreover, the Man in the White Smock has already started to work on the passport of Nadine's father.
Diego gets up and goes to a telephone which is in a corner of the studio.
When they hear the click of the receiver being picked up, Roberto and the Man in the White Smock turn around. Diego is dialing his number.

THE MAN IN THE WHITE SMOCK: Habla en francés, eh?

He is asking Diego to speak French on the phone.

DIEGO: Si, hombre, si!

The Man in the White Smock has resumed his work. Roberto waits without talking while Diego calls Marianne.

Bill? How are you getting on?

(Bill: Is that you, Diego? Do you want to speak to Marianne?)

Yes, can I speak to her, please?

(Marianne: What's the matter?)

Nothing, nothing at all. I'm not leaving.

(Marianne: You mean you are staying with me?)

That's right. I'm staying with you.

(Marianne: You don't sound overly enthusiastic. Are you unhappy?)

Unhappy? No, why would I be unhappy?

(Marianne: Are you staying for a long time?)

He looks around at the studio, at the Man in the White Smock, seen from behind, bent over his work table, at Roberto, seen in profile, impassive: at his friends, his life.

A long time. Maybe forever. We'll go away somewhere, take a vacation.

His laugh is somewhat forced.

(Marianne: Are you coming home now?)

No, not right away.

(Marianne: Tonight, we'll be finished here with our work.)

Tonight, yes, tonight.

(Marianne: I love you, Diego.)

He laughs again, joylessly. He hangs up and stares into space.

RUE DE L'ESTRAPADE. Monday, 3:00 P.M.

Arriving from the Place du Pantheon, Diego emerges into the rue de l'Estrapade. He turns left, remaining on the even-numbered side of the street. He looks across at the opposite sidewalk, the space still separating him from Nadine's house. The sidewalk is empty.

Suddenly, a black Peugeot 404 comes slowly into view, going in the same direction as Diego. The car keeps close to the opposite sidewalk. Inside there are three men, and the one beside the driver is looking out his window checking the numbers of the houses.

Diego is immediately on his guard, his every nerve and muscle reacting to what he senses may be danger. He slows down, his eyes glued to the car, which he dissects into several pieces, as if he were examining the various pieces of a jigsaw puzzle.

The pieces of the puzzle are reassembled, returning to their former unity. The black 404 is driving slowly past Nadine's house.

As soon as it has passed the door, the car slows down even more, and the man in the back seat opens the door and eases himself out. Then the car speeds up and is swallowed by the rue Blainville. The man who has just got out of the 404 is standing motionless on the sidewalk. He lights a cigarette.

Diego sizes him up: he is young, and rather nattily dressed. As he does, he keeps on walking at an even pace. He is now walking past the rear wall of the Lycée Henri IV, on the other side of which is the schoolyard.

He has to make certain. He must find out whether these three men are policemen, if they are watching Nadine's house.

On the small square formed by the intersection of the four streets—the rue de l'Estrapade, Thouin, Blainville, and Tournefort—there are a number of cars parked tightly against one another, forming a kind of protective screen for Diego, behind which he goes and stands, at the corner of the rue de Blainville.

The man who got out of the car has walked now to the corner of the rue d'Ulm. When he reaches the corner, he turns around until he is facing the door to Nadine's house.

Diego glances at his watch. Walking quickly, he turns into the rue Blainville and starts toward the Place de la Contrescarpe.

Halfway there, he passes the man, who is walking in the opposite direction; he thinks he is the one he saw a few moments before sitting next to the driver. He is older, and more conservatively dressed. Diego turns around and sees that the man has stopped at the corner of the rue de Blainville, behind the protective screen of cars where he had been standing a few seconds earlier.

Diego reaches the Place de la Contrescarpe and looks around for the black 404. He slowly circles the square, walking clockwise from the side where the large café with an outdoor terrace is. He soon spots the 404 which is parked at the corner of the rue Lacépède. The driver is reading the newspaper.

Diego turns back and heads toward La Chope café.

The cafés in spring.

The café terraces, in the spring sunshine.

The blond hair of girls one imagines are Swedish and who, sometimes, are from no farther away than the Passy suburbs.

The raised skirts so that the sun can tan the legs, the knees.

The faces raised toward the spring sun, with closed eyes, perhaps the way they are when making love.

The drinks, the drinks of many colors, the siesta drinks, that take the place of the siesta itself.

The immodesty—or perhaps the innocence—of kisses exchanged on the springtime terraces of the cafés.

Diego is at the cash register, asking for a telephone token, waiting for it to be given to him, his eyes feasting on the spectacle of the terraces, of spring, of this terrace during this spring.

Quick cut to Diego in the telephone booth, which is on the ground floor of the café, glass enclosed on all sides so that, depending on one's position inside, one gets a clear view of the square, of the terrace, and of the interior of the café.

He dials a number, his eye taking in as he does the white and yellow eye, the sunflower, the fried egg that a girl at a nearby table on the terrace is just beginning to eat.

The number he has dialed is busy. He hangs up, gets back his token, and waits.

A copy of the weekly news magazine l'Express *has been left by someone on the ledge just below the telephone. Mechanically, he picks it up and leafs through it.*

A page of advertising catches his eye, an advertisement concerning holidays in Spain. "Your own house, on the very edge of the water, on the Costa Brava."

He is looking at the girl on the café terrace, who is also looking at him, at the girl who looks as though she were on vacation, and a parade of mental images begins in his mind. Images of travel bureaus, with their publicity posters; posters in Paris; shots of lines of cars waiting to go through customs at the Spanish border; a rapid montage of tourist photos and filmed shots, all of which relate to tourism in Spain.

He again begins to dial the number he had tried before. Now his whole face is visible in the glass aquarium of the telephone booth.

DIEGO: Nadine?

(Yes. Who's this?)

It's Sunday.

(You're wrong, it's Monday.)

I know it's Monday. I mean it's me who's Sunday.

(I've been waiting for you. Aren't you coming?)

No, I wasn't able to. I have your thing for you.
(Now I've got to go out.)
I remember you had an appointment. Where is your appointment?
(What does that matter. Since you're not coming.)
That's right, I'm not coming. Simply so I know.
(At La Chope café. Do you know where it is?)
La Chope. Yes, I know it.
(You seem to find that funny.)
No, not at all . . . Is six o'clock all right?
(Six is fine. Where?)
Six sharp, in front of the Bullier building.
(Bullier! Why the Bullier building? I'm coming back to the house. Why not here?)
No, I'd prefer that we meet somewhere else. In front of the Bullier building is convenient for me.

He hangs up the phone and remains standing, motionless, in the booth. The girl outside on the café terrace has vanished.

He is wondering whether the boys, or the girls, or the person Nadine is supposed to meet, are already there at La Chope. His gaze scans the café terrace.

Very quick shots of Nadine—laughing, serious, in love—at this or that table, with this or that person, male or female.

He emerges from the telephone booth.

Nadine emerges from the rue Blainville, walking along the even-numbered side of the street. She crosses and comes over toward the terrace of La Chope café.

Shot of Nadine, right profile, her long, lissome stride. Diego is stationed at some distance, on the sidewalk of the rue Mouffetard, just beyond where this street runs into the square.

When he sees Nadine appear, he makes as if to retreat, as though he were afraid she would see him. But Nadine does not turn around. She goes straight to one of the tables on the terrace and sits down opposite a young man, her back to Diego.

Immediately after Nadine appears, the older of the two men who had got out of the 404 comes into view, on the opposite—that is, odd-numbered—side of the street. He also crosses the street, goes into La Chope, and stands at the bar.

Shortly afterward, the younger of the two men whom Diego had spotted looms into sight. He reaches the square, glances around, sees the man at the bar, sees Nadine on the terrace, and goes over and sits down at the nearest table he can find to Nadine and the boy she is with.

Diego takes a few steps, searching for a vantage point from which he can watch them all.

A bum, whom he has hardly noticed till now, suddenly accosts him.

THE BUM: You wouldn't have a cigarette, would you?

Diego takes a package of Gitanes from his coat pocket and starts to give it to the bum, scarcely looking at him as he does. But he interrupts his gesture, opens the package, glances inside. Only then does he hand the package, which he has again closed, to the bum.

Were you looking to make sure there weren't too many left?

Diego laughs, dryly.

DIEGO: Just the contrary. If there had only been one or two left, there was no point in seeming to give you a whole box.

The bum puts out his hand and takes the package.

THE BUM: In that case, O.K.

Diego begins to move away.

Did you see that black 404?

Diego stops in his tracks and looks at him, without offering any comment.

Cops, no question.

Diego shrugs.

DIEGO: I wouldn't know. I don't have much to do with them.

The bum looks at him pensively.

THE BUM: I do. I work for them.

Diego regrets having given away his box of Gitanes.

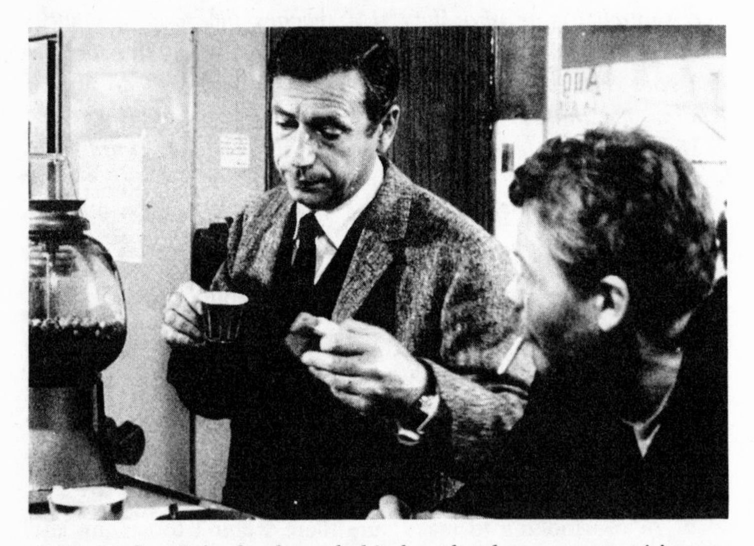

Diego has left the bum behind and taken up a position on the square from which he can keep an eye on the terrace of La Chope café: Nadine, the young man, one of the inspectors seated at a table near them, and the other inside at the bar.

Later, Nadine and the young man leave by the rue Blainville, followed by the younger of the two inspectors. The other goes back to the car, which starts up and drives away, shadowing them down the rue Descartes and the rue Thouin.

Diego has observed all these movements.

Rue Soufflot: Diego, from a distance, invisible, sees Nadine and the young man, who are still being shadowed (the younger inspector following them closely on foot; the car parked on the opposite sidewalk), stop in front of the University Press bookstore.

They walk down the rue Victor Cousin, then turn at the Place de la Sorbonne and wander down the rue Champollion, pausing to look at the publicity pictures posted outside the cinemas.

At a certain point during this game of double shadowing (Nadine and the young man followed by the police inspectors, Diego following everyone), the voices of Diego and Nadine can be heard voice-over.

NADINE'S VOICE: You're wrong, Domingo! Nobody followed me.

DIEGO'S VOICE: Nobody? Are you kidding! There were three of them, with a car.

NADINE'S VOICE: Are you sure?

DIEGO'S VOICE: Listen: I know what I'm talking about. After all, it's my job.

They are in a bookstore on the rue Saint-Severin.
They come out of the store.

They were following you, and I was following them. You didn't notice a thing?

NADINE'S VOICE: I saw some characters looking at me, that I know. But not like that.

They are walking down the rue Danton toward the Boulevard Saint-Germain.

Nadine's laughter.

It does happen to me upon occasion.

Nadine and the young man are in a café at the Odéon intersection, where they meet some friends. They are exchanging small talk together. The police are still shadowing them.

DIEGO'S VOICE: Why do you have the police on your tail?
NADINE'S VOICE: You think they're really police?
DIEGO'S VOICE: Listen, I ought to know.

At the Odéon intersection, Nadine and the young man take leave of each other. He takes the subway, followed by the younger of the two inspectors. The older inspector gets back in the car, without paying any further attention to Nadine, it seems. Nadine leaves, on foot, up the rue de l'Ecole de Médecine.

What is there about you that might interest the police?
NADINE'S VOICE: Nothing.
DIEGO'S VOICE: That's not true.
NADINE'S VOICE: Why are you talking to me like that?
DIEGO'S VOICE: I'm not talking to you like that: I want to know.
NADINE'S VOICE: There's nothing to know.

They are in the Metro: the young man, the inspector, and Diego. Heading toward the Porte d'Orléans.

They were wasting their time, Domingo.
DIEGO'S VOICE: They're still with your boyfriend, at Edgar-

At the Raspail stop, all three get off. They start walking down the boulevard Edgar-Quinet.

NADINE'S VOICE: If they really were police, you shouldn't have made an appointment to meet me. You'll be spotted.

DIEGO'S VOICE: They're still with your boyfriend, at Edgar-Quinet.

Now Nadine and Diego become visible on the screen. They are in the main hall of the Bullier building.

Anxious and disconcerted, Nadine looks at Diego.

NADINE: Miguel?

DIEGO: The boy you were with.

She comes closer, almost shaking him.

NADINE: At Edgar-Quinet?

Diego is immediately alerted by the girl's concern.

DIEGO: You see, you were hiding something.

NADINE: Go on! Tell me what happened!

DIEGO: You left each other at the Odéon intersection. Your friend took the Metro. It was the younger inspector who followed him. We all got off at the Raspail stop, one behind the other.

NADINE: Raspail?

This name alone, and the way she pronounces it, seems to imply a catastrophe of major proportions.

DIEGO: He went into a building on the boulevard Edgar-Quinet.

NADINE: And what about the cop?

DIEGO: He checked the number of the house and then he left. Unless he found another spot farther away to watch from.

Trembling, Nadine begins to move toward the exit.

NADINE: I have to go. They may be going to make a search.

Imploringly, she turns to Diego.

You've got to help me. This is serious. They're also working for Spain, you know.

IN THE VICINITY OF THE RUE DE L'ESTRAPADE. Monday, 7:35 P.M.

Nadine opens the door of the windowed cabin located at the entrance of the garage. There is a light on inside. An old man raises his head, recognizes her, and smiles.

NADINE: I'm taking father's car. I'm going to pick him up at the station later on.

The old man starts to straighten up.

It is still light out, but verging toward dusk. Here and there the fading daylight is already punctuated by electric lights.

The low-slung, massive silhouette, its motor purring, emerges from the garage and turns right.

Not far off, Diego is waiting on the sidewalk. The car slows down. Nadine leans over, reaches out her right arm and opens the door. Diego gets in, stooping down and slipping easily into the car even before she has come to a complete stop.

BOULEVARD EDGAR-QUINET. Monday, 7:45 P.M.

Coming from the direction of Denfert-Rochereau, the Mercedes descends the boulevard Raspail and at the intersection turns into the boulevard Edgar-Quinet, on the even-numbered side of the street. The car is moving slowly. Diego is checking every street corner and door, every sidewalk.

DIEGO: Would you care to tell me what this is all about.

NADINE: I can't, Domingo. Later.

She has called him Domingo, and this name passes above

him, slides past him, unrelated to him. He remains alien to this name, to this entire nocturnal expedition.

He returns to his watch.

DIEGO: I don't see anyone. Drive a little farther, turn left, and come back along the cemetery.

He is above and beyond all this. His voice is precise but uninvolved, routine.

She does as he says. The Mercedes turns left onto a traverse road that cuts across the broad central sidewalk dividing the boulevard Edgar-Quinet. They are on the other side, moving along the wall enclosing the Montparnasse cemetery.

In the last light of day, the gray wall moves slowly past, a ghostlike background. He looks at the wall and has the feeling that it will never end, that it will keep on moving past over and over, as though they were passing the same spot several times.

Turn on your lights.

NADINE: Sorry, I forgot!

She leans forward and touches some button on the dashboard. At first she turns the wrong one, and the bright headlights flash on for a fraction of a second, lighting the wall of the Montparnasse cemetery, at which Diego again glances. But this moving, luminous area on the cemetery wall disappears almost immediately.

They arrive back at the intersection of the boulevard Raspail and boulevard Edgar-Quinet.

DIEGO: You can go.

Nadine steps on the gas, and the well-regulated motor purrs more loudly as the car surges ahead and, where the central sidewalk ends, turns sharply left and begins moving back down the even-numbered side of the street.

How long?

NADINE: I don't know . . . five minutes.

Diego looks at his watch.

DIEGO: I'll pick you up in front of the Delambre cinema. I won't stop; be ready to hop in as I drive by.
NADINE: The registration papers are in the glove compartment. Do you have a driver's license?
DIEGO: Several.
NADINE: I mean a real one.
DIEGO: Yes, even a real one.

Nadine stops next to the sidewalk. She leaves the motor running. She opens the door, lets it close again, and turns back to Diego.

They are motionless, looking at each other.

Go on.

She gets out. Diego shifts over into the driver's seat. He sees Nadine disappear through a door. He looks at his watch and eases the car away from the curb.

QUAI DE BETHUNE. Monday, 8:45 P.M.

He has just closed the door to the apartment. He has closed it by leaning against it with his full weight, and remains with his back to the door.

In his hand he is carrying a small, almost square, ordinary-looking suitcase—and the position of his arm and shoulder, and a certain rigidity of his body, suggest the weight he is supporting.

He is there. A young woman, coming from the living room, passes him on her way to the kitchen carrying a pail of water. She is wearing a blue smock.

THE WOMAN IN BLUE: Buenas tardes!

He sees her pass; he has never seen her before, and is slow to react to her greeting.

DIEGO: Buenas!

But by this time she has already turned the corner into the kitchen and disappeared.

He walks toward the living room and goes in. Marianne,

Agnes, and Bill are seated around a table on which the dummy of the book they are working on is lying.

Three pair of eyes upon him. Bill's: friendly. Agnes': curious. Marianne's: obvious, intent. He is caught by Marianne's gaze. Something has happened. He is there, stupidly, with his suitcase.

AGNES: What's that?
DIEGO: A suitcase.
MARIANNE: Of course it's a suitcase, darling.

And she laughs. She never calls him "darling." She laughs, she calls him "darling," she pretends to be joking: something has happened.

AGNES: It looks heavy.

She looks at it.
Can't she ever shut up?

DIEGO: Papers, papers, and more papers.

He too would have been better off keeping quiet. Something stilted about his words. What papers, why so many papers? He glances at this suitcase, which in fact is heavy, a foreign object, perhaps foreign and hostile too, existing by itself, an unknown object.

Don't let me stop you from working.
MARIANNE: We'll be finished in ten minutes.

Diego nods and goes to leave. At the door he turns back.

DIEGO: Who was that woman I passed in the hall?
MARIANNE: That's Lola.

Shot of Marianne's gaze upon him, transparent. She is thinking of something else. O.K., so that's Lola. He shrugs his shoulders and goes out. In the foyer, he hears Bill's voice overtake him.

BILL'S VOICE: Diego!

He turns around, the suitcase in his hand. Bill closes the living room door behind him and walks over to him.

BILL: I wanted to tell you, about last night . . .

Diego waits for what is to follow. But Bill doesn't know how to phrase what he wanted to say about last night. Silence. Not based on embarrassment this time, but on masculine modesty (which also exists).

I mean, if I can be of any use to you someday . . . A photographer gets to travel, you know.

Diego is looking at him; he nods.

O.K. That's all I wanted to say. I'd better get back before Agnes' curiosity is aroused.

They both laugh. They make some gesture of farewell, each touching the other's arm or shoulder.

In the bedroom, set flat on the bed, the suitcase still looks out of place, even more baffling. Diego has taken off his jacket and is contemplating the object. He tries to open it; it is locked. He goes over to a desk, opens a drawer, and takes out a bunch of small luggage keys. He comes back over and sits down on the bed. He inserts one of the keys into the right-hand lock. It doesn't work. He tries a second. At the sixth or seventh, the lock opens. He had to force it slightly, but the lock opens. He opens the second lock and lifts the top of the suitcase. A piece of burlap completely covers the contents of the suitcase. But even before he takes off the burlap he knows what it contains. He remains motionless a moment, fully aware of what it contains. He removes the burlap. There, neatly lined up in serried rows like so many bars of gold, are several objects of a yellowish color: plastic bombs. Some detonators too, and a length of Bickford rope. With a click, he closes the top of the suitcase containing the plastics.

He is standing: he lifts his fingers to his nose and sniffs: the stubborn smell of the plastics.

When he returns from the bathroom, drying his hands on a towel, Marianne is in the bedroom. The suitcase is still on the bed, closed.

DIEGO: Have you finished?

MARIANNE: Bill took Agnes home. He said we've done enough work for one day.

He tosses the towel over the back of a chair.

What's the matter?

Perhaps Diego is thinking of the suitcase. Perhaps he is thinking that Marianne is thinking of the suitcase too.

DIEGO: Nothing. Why?

MARIANNE: Someone came here, asking for you.

Diego looks at her, on his guard.

The thin dark man you work with, the one who looks as though he hates me.

DIEGO: Why do you say that?

MARIANNE: I don't know, that's the impression I get.

DIEGO: Are you out of your mind?

MARIANNE: I can tell. He distrusts my house, the way I dress, the money I earn. He probably thinks I'm not the right kind of woman for an agent to be with.

DIEGO: So, what did he want?

MARIANNE: He seemed exasperated. He came twice and made me repeat the message word for word. He must think I'm a complete idiot.

She looks him in the eye. She does her best to control her voice, but behind its calm precision is a faint but discernible quiver.

It turns out that everything is changed. You are leaving for Barcelona. Tomorrow in fact. He'll be waiting for you at the same Metro exit as this morning. There will be a meeting to settle questions pertaining to this trip. You'll eat there and leave directly from the meeting. Take your personal effects with you. He'll bring you a passport.

She recites the above the way someone might recite a lesson learned by heart.

DIEGO: Barcelona?

A shot of Juan reappears, briefly and brightly, as though the news of this trip had reactivated the mental mechanism anticipating the future. But the shot of Juan is inextricably mixed with shots of Nadine, of the police he had spotted that afternoon, of Nadine's boyfriend, of the square box of plastics, in a welter of confusion.

Didn't he tell you why I'm leaving?

MARIANNE: That's not exactly his style, you know. He's not a great one for explanations.

Suddenly, Diego explodes in a cold fury.

DIEGO: I'm fed up, fed up, fed up! This morning I had completely lost all political perspective, I was to stay here, take a good rest and think things over, which means discuss matters and prepare my own self-criticism, that's what they really meant. And now all of a sudden I'm still their choice to go to Barcelona, just like that. Well, they'll have to find someone else!

Marianne is watching him. She knows very well that he's going to leave tomorrow, that his explosion of anger far exceeds what he really thinks. But right now she is in no way inclined to get involved in a discussion.

MARIANNE: We don't have to get up at the crack of dawn tomorrow, since you're leaving at noon. Would you like to go out tonight?

Diego looks at her. All his anger is gone. He feels like smiling at her, but he also wants to mark a point.

DIEGO: I thought you said that this was no life?
MARIANNE: I did, this isn't any life.

Now he smiles at her. Now she is laughing, and crying. Now they are in each other's arms.

They were on the bed, in tight embrace, and out of the corner of his eye he sees the suitcase, which reminds him of all his problems.

He sits up.

DIEGO: What do you want to do?
MARIANNE: I don't know. Go to the movies?
DIEGO: Whatever you say.

Again he looks at that suitcase.

MARIANNE: What picture do you want to see?
DIEGO: I don't have any idea what's playing. Pick whatever you want to see.

She goes and gets a newspaper, which she opens to the movie page. She scans the programs.

If you don't mind, before we go to the movies I'd like you to drive me to the station, the gare de Lyon. I want to check this suitcase in the baggage room.

She lowers the newspaper which was hiding her face.

MARIANNE: Why?
DIEGO: Because I want to.
MARIANNE: Can't I know why?
DIEGO: I prefer not to have it here at the house.
MARIANNE: You've always kept your papers here before.
DIEGO: But these I'd prefer not to.

He tries to appear as detached as possible.

MARIANNE: Diego?

He looks at her.

Isn't there anything else?
DIEGO: What else?
MARIANNE: Something you haven't told me.
DIEGO: There's nothing else.

He too gets to his feet.

Or nothing of any consequence, nothing worth talking about.
MARIANNE: I love you, Diego.
DIEGO: I know you do.

THE QUAYS OF THE SEINE. Monday, 9:40 P.M.

They are driving in Marianne's convertible along the quays of the Seine, on the right bank, between the pont de Sully and the embankment road that leads to the gare de Lyon. At an intersection, just before taking this road, the sound of a whistle is heard. Diego is driving. He puts on the brakes.

DIEGO: Is that for us?

Marianne turns around to see what's happening.

MARIANNE: Yes, it's for us.

Diego brings the car to a sudden stop. They both turn around. A policeman is coming toward them. The policeman is beside the left door of the car. Diego leans over to him.

THE POLICEMAN: You used to driving without lights?

Diego looks at his dashboard. The fact is, he has been driving without any lights. He makes a gesture which seems to say: "I'll be damned."

DIEGO: You're right. I forgot.
THE POLICEMAN: Your papers, please.

Diego gestures to Marianne, who rummages in her pocketbook and takes out the registration papers of the car. The Policeman sizes them up, takes the papers.

Is the car yours, Madame?
MARIANNE: Yes, it is.

The Policeman looks at Diego.

THE POLICEMAN: And are you the husband?

DIEGO: No, I'm not the husband.

The Policeman, holding the registration papers in his hand, goes and checks the license plate. He comes back and addresses Diego.

THE POLICEMAN: May I see your license?

Diego takes out his driver's license and gives it to the Policeman, who glances at it.

You're not French?
DIEGO: No, I'm not French.
THE POLICEMAN: You're what nationality?
DIEGO: Spanish.

He pauses.

A Spanish refugee.
THE POLICEMAN: Your identity papers, please!

Diego takes out his wallet again and gives his identity card to the Policeman, who examines it carefully. Then he gives it back to Diego.

Do you know what driving without your lights on could cost you?
DIEGO: No. This is the first time it's happened to me.

The Policeman looks at Marianne.

THE POLICEMAN: You shouldn't let your car be driven by absent-minded people, Madame.

Marianne gives him her broadest smile.

All right, go on. But make sure it doesn't happen again.
MARIANNE: Thank you, sir.

Diego says nothing. He puts his papers away. The car drives away.

THE GARE DE LYON. Monday, 9:50 P.M.

The lighted clock on the station tower of the gare de Lyon reads 9:50 P.M. *Diego is getting out of the car with the heavy suitcase of plastics. The car is parked near the entrance to the main waiting room. Diego takes the suitcase out of the car. Marianne is standing beside him.*

MARIANNE: Wouldn't you like me to go?

Diego seems to hesitate.

Remember what the man said. Don't let absent-minded people carry your suitcase!

They laugh.

DIEGO: All right. Do you know where the lockers are?

She nods. Marianne walks away, carrying the suitcase. Diego lights a cigarette, waits until Marianne has entered the station, and begins to follow her. Inside the station, in front of a long row of ticket windows, Diego sees Marianne making her way through the crowd, walking with her large, purposeful stride. At times he loses sight of her for a fraction of a second in the crowd. Then he finds her again, and his eyes follow her.

Marianne is in front of a group of luggage lockers. She puts the suitcase in an empty locker, locks it and takes the key. On her way back she catches sight of Diego, who has retreated to the cigarette counter, and she starts to run toward him. Suddenly she stops, glances around, and resumes walking. Together they cross the area in front of the station, hand in hand, threading their way among the other cars toward their own. A policeman whistles at a driver who was about to park in a no parking area, and makes a motion for him to move on. When they hear the whistle, Marianne and Diego both burst out laughing.

They are in the car. This time Marianne is behind the wheel. She puts down the top, and Diego gives her a hand.

MARIANNE: "Are you the husband?" "No, I'm not the husband." You should have seen your face when you said that, Diego!

DIEGO: Do I look like a husband?
MARIANNE: I should say not!

She looks at him. Then she looks at him again.

But as for me, I'm your wife.

She turns and kisses him on the mouth.

Come on, let's go to the movies!
DIEGO: Meanwhile we're going to freeze to death!
MARIANNE: It's spring, Diego! A warm, lovely spring!

She bursts out laughing and drives away with a roar.

NEAR THE GARE DE LYON. Monday, 10:00 P.M.

They have driven down the access ramp to the gare de Lyon, and have stopped at a red light. Diego is looking at the lights of the café, at the life and movement of the neighborhood. The light turns green and Marianne steps on the gas. As she does, Diego says:

DIEGO: Let me out at the café.

Marianne puts on the brakes, looks to see there is nothing behind her, puts on her right signal light.

The car is parked, not far from a neighborhood movie house. Marianne turns to Diego with a questioning look.

I have to make a call.
MARIANNE: Right now. Before the movie?

He begins to open the door on his side. Marianne watches him in silence. He has got out of the car. He leans down to Marianne. Her worried face is raised toward him.

DIEGO: It'll only take a minute.

He takes two steps, then comes back to the car. Marianne's eyes have remained glued on him.

Did Manolo say 11:00?
MARIANNE: What? Oh, the small thin fellow. Yes, 11:00 sharp.

DIEGO: I'll be right back.

He walks away toward one of the cafés at the intersection.

*

The telephone is on the bar. There is a great deal of noise around him as he talks.

DIEGO: I'm sorry to bother you at this time of night, Monsieur. May I please speak to Nadine.

(. . . . .)

Thanks very much.

Nadine? It's me.

(. . . . .)

I have to see you tomorrow. You and your friends both, without fail.

(. . . . .)

That's right, without fail.

(. . . . .)

Tomorrow afternoon will be too late.

(. . . . .)

What?

(. . . . .)

Too late for everything.

(. . . . .)

At nine o'clock in the morning. At the Metro stop where I left you earlier tonight.

(. . . . .)

Downstairs, on the station platform, on the Etoile side.

(. . . . .)

Without fail, Nadine.

He hangs up. He is pensive. He lights a cigarette.

*

He is back in the car, getting back into the front seat. Shot of Marianne's eyes upon him. Around them, the sounds and sights of the nocturnal neighborhood, people passing the movie house, pausing to look at the publicity pictures posted outside.

MARIANNE: What's the matter with you, Diego?

She has turned on the motor.

DIEGO: Nothing! I had to arrange for someone to pick up that suitcase, that's all.

She has put the car into first, it slowly starts to move, she shifts into second, but it is still going slowly.

MARIANNE: Couldn't that wait? Manolo could just have easily picked that suitcase up at the house!

As she drives, she glances over at him.

DIEGO: Do you mind if I organize my work the way I want to?

He lights a cigarette and looks away: at the night, the trees, the houses. At nothing.

MARIANNE: As a matter of fact, it's not only that suitcase. . . . Do you want me to tell you?

He turns to her.

DIEGO: I don't want anything, but since you're going to tell me anyway, go ahead.

Marianne has again stopped the car (this time, as before, being very careful to signal her stop by putting on her right signal light). She puts on the hand brake and turns to Diego.

MARIANNE: Last night you wanted to leave for Barcelona, to catch up with Juan. But you were already worried and upset. You exploded in front of Bill and Janine. You, who are always so careful, do you think that's the way UNESCO interpreters talk? And then this noon you announced you weren't leaving. You said: "I'm staying with you," but you were sad. What happened this morning?

DIEGO: This morning?

MARIANNE: At your meeting . . .

There is a silence; he stares out into the night.

I have the feeling you're not sure where you're going, Diego, that you're confused, lost.

DIEGO: I know where I'm going. I'm going to Barcelona. I presume I'm supposed to go with Juan to Madrid. And then come back here. I have to get some rest, they want to talk to me. You know, in Spain I see things from too close a viewpoint, I'm blinded by reality. I have to get a new view of the total picture, even if it's unreal.

MARIANNE: I don't know what you're talking about any more.

DIEGO: My comrades are completely convinced that some day the whole thing is going to blow sky high, and that day is not far off. I know only too well: no one can resign himself to dying in exile. But it's not true. There's still a very long march ahead of us.

MARIANNE: No, it's impossible! It's true that it has to be blown sky high!

DIEGO: You think so! Listen to this.

He has taken from his pocket the paper he was given at the meeting that morning. It's a copy of Euzkadi Obrera, *the clandestine paper—printed in small format on Bible paper—of the Communist party in the Basque country.*

The camera pauses at the first page of the paper, explores the headlines and comes to a complete stop on a call to arms, printed in bold type in the middle of the page. It's an appeal for a general strike.

Diego reads the translation to Marianne.

"Various opposition forces in the Basque region have mutually decided to call for a general strike starting April 30th at 8:00 A.M. Students will also take part in it. The strike will go on for one week, and, if repressive measures are taken, will continue for an unlimited period. . . ."

Diego folds the newspaper and puts it back in his pocket.

All that is nonsense. It's a kind of magic language, abracadabra, as though you were parading idols to make it rain.

MARIANNE: No it's not. I hope this general strike will really take place.

DIEGO: There will be isolated incidents here and there, tiny factions. But all in all, nothing. This is an unreal action.

MARIANNE: I hope you're wrong! I believe the strike will take

place! Isn't that what you've been hoping for all these years? Isn't that why your friends are dead or in prison?

He says nothing, staring into the night.

I hope you're wrong, that you really have been blinded! Things *have* to change, so that you can go back to Spain and I can go with you, so that we can live!

DIEGO: It doesn't do any good to cry or shout. The reality of the situation remains the same.

Behind them, a car signals with its lights. We also hear the short beep of a horn. Because Marianne has inadvertantly parked in front of a porte-cochere. She makes a sign that she has understood and starts up the motor. The car moves away.

MARIANNE: Shall we go home?
DIEGO: Yes, let's go home.

Quai de Bethune. Marianne is locking the car doors, after having put up the top. Diego walks over to the Seine and leans on the parapet. He hears Marianne's footsteps behind him.

MARIANNE'S VOICE: What are you doing?
DIEGO: Nothing. Staring into the night.

He turns around till he is facing her. They both stand looking at each other. She comes over and stands very close to him.

MARIANNE: I really must have a child by you, Diego. Otherwise I'll go mad.

He has taken her in his arms.

DIEGO: If I were to go back to Spain and start all over again from zero, would you come with me?
MARIANNE: To Spain? You mean, go back to Spain right now, normally. With real identity papers?
DIEGO: That's right, normally. With real honest-to-God identity papers.

He smiles at her.

I didn't become a permanent agent to spend my life in Aubervilliers or Ivry, going from meeting to meeting. I find it impossible to get used to . . . Anyway, one ought to be in Spain. That's where the action is.
MARIANNE: Do you think it's possible? Do you think the police don't know your real identity?
DIEGO: They certainly have heard of Carlos. But for them Diego Mora is a complete stranger.
MARIANNE: In that case we'll go to Spain.

Shot of the enveloping night, as they walk arm in arm.

IV

A Slow, Stubborn Task of Edification Which Goes on Indefinitely

AT THE RASPAIL METRO STOP. Tuesday, 9:00 A.M.

The sun.

The sun, directly ahead, almost in his eyes when he looks at the entrance to the Raspail Metro station. A vision of the Metro entrance, shimmering in the sunlight: the top of the Metro steps; the bodies of the people emerging and descending; the huge whale of the Metro devouring and spewing forth human bodies. A steady vision, like that of a steady gaze, aimed fixedly at a motionless framework: this Metro entrance, this newspaper stand, a corner of the street opposite, perhaps a tree. A frozen frame, into which and out of which people suddenly enter and leave, fleeting apparitions, ghosts materialized from the void, destined to disappear completely.

And the sun. The sun, directly ahead, almost in his eyes.

He has had to move, take refuge from this sun, suddenly hot: the picture becomes clearer, less blinded by this sun in his eyes.

The frozen frame of the picture, sometimes empty, with the multicolored spots of the weekly magazines displayed at the newsstand, sometimes filling with people in a hurry or nonchalant, emerging from the void of the Metro or being swallowed up into this avid maw.

Now, the shadow of this subterranean mouth into which we plunge as he does.

The central area of the station, then the corridors. He sees the sign: ETOILE. *He was going to pass the sign, without paying any attention, caught up in the routine of predetermined patterns, when something happens.*

Is it the word ETOILE? *Is it this word which has set something in motion?*

ETOILE, ETOILE, ETOILE, *as though this ordinary, undistinctive sign—a few black letters on a grayish background—had become some kind of fireworks, an explosion of luminous letters, lighting up and going out at irregular and unpredictable intervals, sometimes horizontal but also diagonal and vertical as well.*

ETOILE, ETOILE, ETOILE, *like a luminous message from somewhere and, for the moment, incomprehensible. A message which, throughout the day, is going to make its way within you until it becomes absolutely clear, absolutely readable, when it has reached full fruition.*

ETOILE, ETOILE, ETOILE.

After this message has exploded in the darkness of the station, the darkness of his brain, he has stopped at the top of the stairs leading down to the station platform.

He is motionless, after the explosion of this message, which is still unreadable. He begins walking again.

At the end of the station platform, sitting very stiffly on the bench like some little girl, is Nadine.

NADINE: Why did you open the suitcase, Domingo?

She is staring straight in front of her. She is smoking. A train of cars stops on the opposite track.

DIEGO: With things like that, I don't like to be lied to.

NADINE: I didn't lie. I asked you to keep a suitcase for me, that's all.

DIEGO: It was plastics.

She is staring into space.

NADINE: Does that frighten you?

He gives a short laugh, which he intends to be insulting, to hurt.

DIEGO: You dumb little bitch! I was carrying suitcases like that when I was seventeen.

NADINE: So was I.

A train of cars stops on the same track where they are sitting. Nadine's words were calm, as though they were taken for granted.

Shots of the people in the Metro.

Without a word Nadine and Diego have turned toward each other. There is a trace of a smile, suddenly childish, on Nadine's lips.

Hello!

He can't keep from smiling too.

DIEGO: Hello!

A Metro sweeper passes by, watering the platform from his metal watering can. He looks at them. He is an old man, who looks gentle and kindly. She is looking at him, but we cannot really tell whether her look is in any way related to this conversation or whether he is, quite simply, the object of her attention.

Tell me, how did you get mixed up with Spain?

NADINE: And what about you?

He gives a short laugh.

DIEGO: It's my country, after all!

NADINE: You mean to say we don't have any right to get mixed up with your country, Domingo? Every man for himself, each in his own corner! Would you prefer that we confined ourselves to questions relating to UNEF, our little student problems, the price of eggs in Paris? I thought we were internationalists!

He laughs again and puts a hand on her shoulder.

DIEGO: Internationalism means first putting your own revolution in order in your own country.

NADINE: My father lends you his passport, and I carry suitcases.

Diego gets up.

DIEGO: Which reminds me. Let's go talk about that suitcase.

Still seated, she remains staring at him for a long moment.

They are at the corner of the boulevard Edgar-Quinet. Diego stops, and Nadine, who had taken a few steps, turns back to him.

Here, your father's passport.

He hands her an envelope, which she half opens. She takes the passport from it.

What floor is it on?

Nadine looks at him with surprise.

NADINE: Why? Aren't you coming with me?

DIEGO: You go in first, alone. I'll follow you.

Nadine pouts, perhaps expressing disdain, perhaps simply disappointment.

NADINE: Don't you trust me?
DIEGO: Listen: the way and time I go or leave somewhere is for me to decide.

Again he has been cutting. Meekly, Nadine leaves.

IN AN APARTMENT ON THE BOULEVARD EDGAR-QUINET, WHICH OVERLOOKS THE MONTPARNASSE CEMETERY. Tuesday, 9:15 A.M.

Diego raises a curtain and sees a view of the Montparnasse cemetery, from this window fronting on the boulevard Edgar-Quinet.

He stares for a long moment at the landscape.

He lets the curtain fall and turns around.

A young man, hardly out of adolescence, whose fair hair is a shade too long, who is dressed with studied nonchalance (leather, or corduroy, perhaps), a rather handsome young man with blue eyes, looks at him, smiling.

THE YOUNG MAN: I gather from your expression you don't like cemeteries.

Diego has had previous experience with this kind of willfully provocative, somewhat juvenile opening gambit.

He looks at the person who has spoken.

He looks past the fair-haired young man, who is seated on a chair next to a round table, at the arrangement of the room. It is a baroque, end-of-the-century room, overly furnished, the furniture and objects too ornate, the colors not matching. A setting that contrasts with the extreme youth, the candid faces and shining eyes of Nadine's friends.

There is the young, fair-haired boy, first of all. Then, slightly behind, the boy who had been with Nadine the day before, whom she had called Miguel. He is dark and more solemn—

that is, his physical appearance makes him seem more solemn. He is sitting in an easy chair. In the middle of the room, directly in the line of Diego's gaze, on a curiously mauve sofa, Nadine is sitting next to another girl.

Diego's gaze has taken in the entire room.

Still, it gives you a clear view. It lets a little sunshine into your life.

At that, Diego bursts out laughing. It is not in any way a forced laugh, but spontaneous and joyful. He suddenly feels at ease, on the same level as these young people with whom he does not agree because he fails to believe in the efficacity of plastic bombs in Spain, but with whom he basically agrees on a deeper level: isn't it true that, in one way or another, this hypocritical and enclosed society has to be burst wide open?

At first his laugh disconcerts the others. But they realize there is nothing insulting about it, that it's not sardonic.

Diego's laugh becomes infectious. He walks to the center of the room, toward the table.

DIEGO: What exactly do you stand for?

All of a sudden his tone has become cutting, slightly superior.

THE YOUNG MAN: What?

Diego is still standing, towering above them. He lights a cigarette.

DIEGO: I mean, you're not hoarding plastic bombs for your own pleasure, are you? Are you a group, an organization, do you have a program?

THE YOUNG MAN: We're the Leninist group, "Revolutionary Action."

He was very loud and brash in making this declaration; but also touching. Diego looks at him.

DIEGO: Of course. Everyone's a Leninist these days.

The boy who was with Nadine the day before breaks in. Diego turns to him.

MIGUEL: Listen, we're not going to get bogged down in a discussion of theory. Nadine gave you a suitcase to keep. What do you plan to do with it?

He used the formal "vous" form of address. He speaks impeccable French. But lurking somewhere in his speech pattern is a certain musicality that makes it different. Maybe he's Spanish.

DIEGO: I could have thrown it in the Seine and disappeared. But the truth is I'm curious to know what tactics you prescribe in Spain.

He looks at them all and realizes that he must make something else quite clear.

I wanted to tell you: I'm here on a purely personal basis.

The Young Man glances at the other three, in silent mutual consultation.

NADINE: Go on, tell him.

Diego has sat down at the table, facing the Young Man. Behind him, slightly to his right, is Nadine and the other girl, seated on the sofa. Even further to the right, but physically closer than the sofa, is Nadine's boyfriend, in his easy chair, attentive.

The Young Man leans forward and begins his explanation.

THE YOUNG MAN: For the past twenty-five years Spain has been in a latent prerevolutionary situation. . . .

Some time has gone by. Now, the young leader of the "Revolutionary Action" group is about to tackle the conclusion of his statement.

Let me sum up: Tourism is one of the main sources of income for the regime. But there is another side to it: millions of people are getting used to the notion that Spain is a perfectly normal country. They tend to associate Spain with their vacation memories, which are necessarily pleasant. This is an extremely dangerous factor of political mystification, of demobilizing anti-Fascist action in Europe. We therefore have to strike a blow at tourism in Spain. Create a climate which will stop it, or at least slow it up. . . .

Diego has gotten to his feet, is pacing the floor. But the Young Man refuses to be impressed. He continues speaking, not in the least upset.

We obtain a double result: we stop the flow of foreign exchange, and we awaken the conscience of the masses.

DIEGO: You mean because it's asleep?

The Young Man looks at him.

THE YOUNG MAN: Sorry, that's not what I meant. I say that, objectively speaking, there exists in Spain a revolutionary situation. But there are no revolutionary politics, no revolutionary front. Lenin said . . .

DIEGO: Lenin's no prayer mill.

His words were cutting. The Young Man looks at him, searching for another angle of attack.

THE YOUNG MAN: But your peaceful means amount to pure revisionism! Objectively speaking, you're following in the wake of the Spanish bourgeoisie.

Diego cannot keep from smiling.

DIEGO: Objectively speaking?

THE YOUNG MAN: That's right, objectively speaking.

DIEGO: And that's why, for the past twenty-five years, they've been chasing us, throwing us in prison, pushing us out of windows, shooting us, that the sentences imposed on us are always the heaviest? Because, objectively speaking, we placed ourselves in the service of the bourgeoisie?

His voice is a notch louder. Nadine's boyfriend, without moving from where he is sitting, breaks in.

MIGUEL: He said "following in the wake of," not "in the service of." He was using a political concept which you're transforming into a moral judgment.

Diego has been listening to him carefully.

DIEGO: That's true, you're right.

MIGUEL: We're not questioning either the ability or the heroism of your militant members. What we do question is your basic political approach.

Diego is looking at him.

DIEGO: For instance?

MIGUEL: For instance: you've again passed the word that there will be a general strike on April 30th. And again you're courting failure.

Diego is looking at him thoughtfully.

DIEGO: You seem pretty categorical.

MIGUEL: I'm just basing what I say on past experience. Since 1959, every general strike that has been called has ended in failure.

Diego stirs uncomfortably. Didn't he say precisely the same thing to Marianne?

DIEGO: Since '59? That makes how long? Eight years. The validity of any strategical tactic cannot be judged over so short a period. You're not very patient, for people who want to make a revolution.

But Nadine's boyfriend comes back to his primary concern.

MIGUEL: What if we were to talk instead about that suitcase?

DIEGO: Yes, let's do. That asinine bit almost got me arrested by the cops.

Silent reaction by the young people: they look at him as though he had said something very stupid. They look at each other, too.

MIGUEL: And what if it were the other way around?

He has spoken very calmly, sure of himself. Diego seems taken aback.

THE YOUNG MAN: Yes! Who was it that brought the police to Nadine's? You, that is the person that used René Sallanches' passport!

MIGUEL: The police began to tail us from Nadine's house, because of that incident at the border. That's the only hypothesis that holds water.

THE YOUNG MAN: What matters is to know how long you've been followed. The Spanish police must have alerted the French. In any case, they can't touch us.

MIGUEL: We haven't done anything. . . .

Diego, beside himself with rage, looks at Nadine, beside himself with rage that she has revealed everything.

The possibility the young people have raised is pregnant with possibilities. At what point was he first spotted, and since when has he been followed, by the police? Since Madrid?

His mental images superimpose themselves over the reality of this room on the boulevard Edgar-Quinet.

*

Images of himself—slightly out of focus, slightly jerky—walking along a street impossible to identify, as though he had been filmed by a hand-held camera, by someone who possibly might have followed him in a car.

Some still photographs of himself, in a raincoat as it is raining, in a jacket in good weather, long shots at first, then close-ups taken with a telephoto lens.

Interspersed among these images are the faces of policemen: unknown policemen with little mustaches, obviously Spanish; Inspector Ledoux, from Behobie; the younger inspector who followed Nadine and her boyfriend.

*

He is on his feet, his face expressionless, livid: his anger, perhaps, is directed against himself.

DIEGO: In any case, all the groups who wanted to play at terrorism have been grilled before they knew what was happening.

He takes a few steps away from the table, turning his back to them. He takes out a cigarette, which he bites without lighting. He comes back toward them.

And besides, what in Christ do you think I need your plastics for? Eat it?

The others say nothing. Perhaps they realize that his anger is aimed at himself, at the situation he's gotten himself into. He tosses a key onto the table.

It's in one of the lockers at the gare de Lyon. And I hope you blow yourselves up with it!

He moves away from them, toward the door. He exits without turning around and slams the door behind him.

As he starts to walk down the staircase leading into the Raspail Metro station, the hurried sound of high heels makes him look back. Nadine is running toward him.

She is one step higher than he on the Metro stairs, so that their faces are on the same level. She looks at him.

NADINE: You left, just like that!

They are motionless.

Diego's hand is on the railing that divides the staircase into two sections, one for those ascending, the other for those going down.

DIEGO: I'm going to be late.
NADINE: Will you call me? Tonight?

Diego shakes his head.

They sense a presence and both turn around. An old lady is climbing the stairs, leaning on the hand rail. They are blocking her way. The old lady gives them a withering look, but says nothing.

They stand aside to let her past. The old lady passes, pauses two steps higher up, and turns back to them.

THE OLD LADY: Really, you might be a little more considerate of an old lady like me!

Nadine and Diego glance at each other, smiling.

NADINE: Will you call me tomorrow?

He shakes his head. He says nothing.

Are you leaving?

Suddenly she has understood.
Her voice is different.
He still says nothing.

Will you call me when you get back?

He says nothing.

Are you coming back?

He says nothing. He leaves.

IVRY. Tuesday, 11:25 A.M.

Diego, carrying his handbag, goes into the elevator of that building in Ivry where the meeting was held yesterday.

Yesterday? Was it yesterday? His face is smooth, inscrutable, almost without expression. He emerges from the elevator and walks down the hallway. He rings, the way Roberto did yesterday, at the same door, in the same way: two short rings, then one long.

He waits before the door, which opens abruptly. It is Roberto who has opened it. He is excited, angry. He motions for Diego to come in.

ROBERTO: Qué te ha pasado?

He wants to know what has happened to Diego. He closes the door.

DIEGO: Nada, ahora te explico.

He says that nothing has happened, that he will explain it to him. Roberto taps the wrist on which he wears his watch.

ROBERTO: Veinte minutos de retraso!

Twenty minutes late! Roberto finds this inexcusable.

DIEGO: Bueno, bueno, aqui estoy. . . .

Diego offers no explanation, nothing, nor gives any excuse. He simply says that there's no problem, stop worrying, that he's there.

He goes into the living room.

Manolo is near the window, looking outside. He turns around; he seems sad.

On the open table are spread out some papers, the map of a city—Barcelona.

Manolo seems preoccupied as he watches Diego come in.

NARRATOR'S VOICE: You didn't know that Ramon was dead, they're going to announce the news to you in a second. Dead Sunday night, a few hours after you saw him. His heart gave out, as the saying goes. Ramon wanted to go to Barcelona, to get away from the routine, the obscure work he had been doing for the past fifteen years: preparing double-bottomed suitcases, automobiles arranged to carry contraband. And now you're going to leave in his place, because the work has to go on, no single death can interrupt it.

All three of them standing around the table, Roberto and Manolo tell Diego of Ramon's death. All three of their faces are tense, hurt. Diego is still carrying his handbag.

Now they are seated around the table. Manolo is showing Diego the location of a street on the map of Barcelona.

MANOLO: Aribau, 45, tercero derecha.
DIEGO: La contraseña?

They are telling him the address of the house where he will find Juan, and he asks what the password is.

MANOLO: El sol se levanta por Benidorm.

Diego notes all this on a piece of paper which, a short while hence, he will tear into tiny pieces and burn in the ashtray. He is writing it down simply to remember it better.

DIEGO: Cuando es el entierro?

He suddenly asks when Ramon's funeral will be held.

They are around the table, around the map of Barcelona spread out before them, discussing questions relating to the trip. But Diego takes leave of this real, mortal setting and, in his imagination, is at the Montparnasse cemetery, behind Ramon's coffin, next to the open grave. Ramon's wife passes by and tosses some flowers on the open grave.

MANOLO: Esta mañana hemos tenido carta de Madrid. Las cosas no son tan graves como parecía.

Manolo says that they have received news from Madrid and that things do not seem to be as serious as they first seemed.

ROBERTO: También en Madrid habra huelga, el 30 de abril! Y el Primero de Mayo, a la Gran Via!

Roberto says that there will also be a strike in Madrid, on April 30th. And the 1st of May, demonstrations on the Gran Via.

Diego sees himself, earlier that morning, defending this strike in which he does not believe, to Nadine and her friends.

NARRATOR'S VOICE: Ramon never saw Spain, the country of his parents. You're going to look at the trees on the mall, the vineyards on the hillsides, this trip, with Ramon's eyes. Throughout this trip, you're going to feel the pleasure Ramon would have felt.

Now, in Diego's mind, they are in front of Ramon's house in Issy-les-Moulineaux. Besides Diego, Manolo and Roberto are there, and Ramon's wife Carmen too, a small group of men and women. The funeral parlor employees are carrying Ramon's coffin, carrying it through the iron gate.

You didn't know that Ramon was dead. There was shadow, some trees, sunshine, and Ramon was dead. Death brings a little sunlight into your life: that's what they told you a little while ago. You laughed, and should have shouted, told him to shut up, because Ramon was dead, and it's Ramon's shadow that has entered your life. The shadow of death, which has been upon you since the day you were born.

He is with Manolo, with Roberto, they are talking. But at the same time, in his mind's eye, they are around a freshly dug grave in a suburban cemetery. A man unfurls a flag, which till then he had kept rolled around its staff. The faded colors of the Spanish Republic unfurl in the cemetery.

You think that there won't be any strike in Madrid, on April 30th. But you're caught up again by the fraternity of long combats, by the stubborn joy of the action.

Behind the unfurled flag of the Spanish Republic, a small crowd has set off marching.
But it is not the same cemetery. There are cypress trees, the sea in the background. It would now appear as though they are marching toward a festival, a victory, behind this unfurled flag.

You are going to find Juan, you are going to go with him to Madrid. One last time, you are going to knock at doors, unknown people will open them, you will say something, anything, that the sun is rising over Benidorm, or that the almond trees are in flower in Antonio's garden, and they will ask you in, you will be together, for these are the passwords.

You are going to look at everything with Ramon's eyes, the sky, the vineyards, and the unknown people's faces. You are going to feel all the joy Ramon would have felt, as if this were your first trip, as if the battle were beginning today.

All three of them—Diego, Manolo, and Roberto, are eating. The door opens and a young man comes in.

ROBERTO: Hello, Pierrot!
DIEGO: Hello, Pierrot, hello!
PIERROT: The buddy's downstairs. He's waiting with the car.

The young man they call Pierrot hands Diego an envelope of thick brown paper.

Diego is in the hallway, about to leave. Roberto is walking with him. Diego opens the envelope he has been given, takes a passport from it, opens it and looks inside.

DIEGO: Dammit!
ROBERTO: What's the matter?

Roberto is worried.

DIEGO: Nothing. My name's Chauvin.

He laughs. Roberto looks at him, uncertain whether to smile or scowl. It is far from certain that he appreciates this quirk of fate. Roberto is a serious-minded person.

ON A STREET IN IVRY. Tuesday, 2:00 P.M.

Diego is putting his bag into the trunk of a convertible. A man is standing next to him who then closes and locks the trunk. A young, well-dressed man. They are facing each other.

THE MAN: My name is Sarlat. André Sarlat.
DIEGO: And mine is Chauvin, Gabriel.
THE MAN: Damn! That's one helluva name.

They laugh and get into the car.

DIEGO: Shall we tell each other the story of our lives once we get started?
THE MAN: The real story or the false?

They laugh.

DIEGO: I'll tell the false. The real one is of no importance.

THE MAN: We have to get going, it seems. So let's go. You'll have to fill me in on a few things. This is my first time.

DIEGO: You'll see, it's simple.

Again they laugh. Diego lays his hand for a second on the man's shoulder.

So, shall we get going?

They laugh, both of them, already fraternal, already accomplices, already together.

He is in a car again, a passenger again.

Just as the car starts up, the image of Juan is seen projected in the windshield.

They are gone.

V

To Warn Diego

RUE DE L'ESTRAPADE. At Nadine Sallanches'. Tuesday, 4:00 P.M.

The face of a stranger, a man about forty years old, fills the entire screen. A motionless face, with a look that misses nothing.

NADINE'S VOICE: My father came back Sunday night.

They are in the living room of the Sallanches' apartment, which looks out onto the rue de l'Estrapade.

The man moves slightly toward Nadine, who is standing near the table.

THE INSPECTOR: Ah! The concierge told me it was Monday.

Nadine gives a childish laugh.

NADINE: She's a bit old, you know, she mixes everything up.
THE INSPECTOR: I see.

He said that without any implication, a simple rejoinder. But Nadine is vaguely worried, wondering what he is driving at.

I'm sorry he's not here. I would merely have liked to glance for a moment at his passport.

Nadine makes a rapid movement with her hand, as though relieved.

NADINE: That's no problem. His passport is right here in his desk!

She has said that without thinking. She looks at the man and wonders how things are going to turn next.

On an unspecified road, the car bearing Gabriel Chauvin and his driver is seen speeding along.

The passport is open, on the table, and the man is studying the photo of René Sallanches.

A shot of Diego's and Sarlat's faces, seen through the windshield, talking together as the car speeds along.

The Inspector—for he is, beyond any shadow of doubt, a plainclothesman—closes the passport and hands it to Nadine, as he straightens up. His face betrays no sign of emotion.

THE INSPECTOR: Well, everything seems in order. I'm sorry to have disturbed you, Mademoiselle.

Nadine looks at him.

A shot of Diego's face, of him alone, seen through the windshield.

The police Inspector takes a few steps toward the door. He stops, turns around, and says:

Last Sunday we received an alert about a car, and a passenger in that car. A car which had been spotted in Madrid. They let him out of the country with the Frenchman who was driving him, because they were sure they could pick him up when he came back into Spain. At least that was their story! Because if your father's passport is here, it can't be wandering around somewhere else, right? One more piece of false information.

He smiles strangely, takes a few more steps.

In any case, politics is always a complicated affair. There are people involved in some clandestine operation, like that, and one morning you wake up and find out they've become a minister.

Nadine races through the apartment like one insane, bumping into walls, doors, furniture, until she gets to the telephone.

Diego and Sarlat, in the car, whose top they have now put down, driving at top speed through the spring sunlight, the spring wind.

Nadine dials a number.

Diego and Sarlat in the car, laughing. Images of sunlight and wind, in spring.

Nadine is speaking into the phone.

NADINE: Daddy? You've got to warn your friends.
(What are you talking about, Nadine? What friends?)
Domingo's friends.
(Domingo? Can't you be a little clearer?)
The passport. They came for the passport.
(Can't you come over here, Nadine?)
Yes, you're right, I'm coming. I'll be right over.

Nadine runs, like one insane, toward the door to the apartment.

She comes back; she had forgot her key.

She leaves again, on the run.

It's late at night.

Salat's car stops at the French side of the border control, at Perthus. A French customs official comes up to the car, takes the passports, and stamps them with a metal stamp.

ORLY AIRPORT. Wednesday, 11:30 A.M.

The movement of the custom official's hand is followed immediately by an identical gesture on the part of an Air France clerk stapling a baggage check onto a plane ticket.

THE CLERK: You're in luck, Madame. A last-minute cancellation just came through.

Marianne is at this Air France ticket window above which is a sign which reads: BARCELONA.

A shot of the vast expanse of glass, steel, of smooth, polished, brightly gleaming surfaces, which echo, buzz, crackle with the sound of loudspeakers calling plane departures or arrivals, the resonant echo of heels on stone.

Marianne is still at the Air France ticket window, as the clerk hands her her ticket.

No luggage? Immediate boarding, one flight up.

Marianne takes her ticket and boarding pass.

Have a pleasant trip, Madame.

He has spoken in a pleasant tone of voice, routinely pleasant. But Marianne is looking at him, suddenly confused, prey to a violent emotion, suddenly shaking like a leaf.

She is almost running, in the sound-filled space of Orly terminal.

Just before she reaches the turnstiles leading to the stairways up to the departure area, Manolo—the thin, swarthy member of the group—is waiting for Marianne.

She stops beside him.

MANOLO: All set?

MARIANNE: Yes, I have my ticket.

MANOLO: Are you clear about everything? You remember what we said?

MARIANNE: Perfectly.

MANOLO: The address of the house, what you have to say?

MARIANNE: 45, rue Aribau, third floor right. I ask to speak to Teresa, and I tell her that the sun is rising over Benidorm.

MANOLO: And you tell them not to go to Madrid. That both of them, Juan and Diego, should come straight back here, right? But by different routes.

MARIANNE: That's it: to come back.

MANOLO: I don't understand why Carlos didn't say anything to us about that incident at the border the other day. Anyway, we'll see when he gets back.

Then Manolo smiles at her. It's the first time she's seen him smile.

But everything will work out. You have just enough time, but it will all work out. Buen viaje.

Marianne smiles back.

MARIANNE: Thanks.

She ascends the escalator, with the sounds of the airport, the interminable loudspeaker, echoing around her.

She is in the upstairs waiting room, looking at the big board on which arrivals and departures are announced.

She almost runs toward the passport control point. She shows her passport to the customs official, who absently stamps it.

She almost runs down the long, interminable corridor in this vast expanse of glass and steel, this luminous cage, toward a little red light blinking on and off in the distance.

She runs toward that blinking light, which announces the imminent departure of the Caravelle for Barcelona, toward the face of Diego, which appears and disappears, dizzily, in the depths of her heart.

Credits

A French-Swedish Co-production:
Sofracima, Paris; Europa-Film, Stockholm

Yves Montand	Diego
Ingrid Thulin	Marianne

With

Geneviève Bujold	Nadine Sallanches
Jean Dasté	The Chief

And in order of appearance on the screen

Dominique Rozan	Jude
Jean-François Remi	Juan
Marie Mergey	Mme. Lopez
Jacques-Wallet	A C.R.S. Policeman
Michel Piccoli	First Inspector
Anouk Ferjac	Mme. Jude
Roland Monod	Antoine
Pierre Decazes	A S.C.N.F. Employee
Paul Crauchet	Roberto
Claire Duhamel	A Traveler
Antoine Bourseiller	Another Traveler
Laurance Badie	Bernadette Pluvier
Françoise Bertin	Carmen
Yvette Etievant	Yvette
Jean Bouise	Ramon
Annie Fargue	Agnes
Gérard Sety	Bill
Catherine de Seynes	Jeanine
Jacques Rispal	Manolo
Fylgia Zadig	Woman at the Meeting
Pierre Leproux	Man in the White Smock
Roger Pelletier	Second Inspector
R. J. Chauffar	A Drunkard
José-Maria Flotats	Miguel
Jean Bolo	An Agent
Pierre Barbaud	A Client
Gérard Lartigau	Head of "Revolutionary Action"
Jean Larrouquette	A Member of "Revolutionary Action"
Martine Vatel	A Student
Paillette	An Old Lady
Jacques Robnard	Pierrot
Marcel Cuvelier	Inspector Chardin
Bernard Fresson	Sarlat
Antoine Vitez	A Pan-Am Employee

Scenario Jorge Semprun

Direction Alain Resnais

Photography Sacha Vierny

Cameraman Philippe Brun

Assistants Robert Alliel, Pierre Li

Settings Jacques Saulnier

Property Manager Charles Merangel

Assistant Jean-Jacques Caziot

Assistants to the Director Jean Léon, Florence Malraux

Script-girl Sylvette Baudrot

Sound Antoine Bonfanti

Assistants Robert Cambourakis, Urban Loiseau

Editing Eric Pluet

Assistants Hadassa Misrahi, Ziva Postec

Production Manager Alain Tueffelean

Assistants Jean Pieuchot, Louis Lliberia

Make-up Alex Marcus, Eliane Marcus

Stills Nicole Lala

Property Man Louis Charpeaux

Head Electrician Yves Laurent

Head Grip René Pequinot

Second Unit George Houssaye

Wardrobe Madeleine Lafon

Production Secretary Blanche Cochet

Accountant Odette Hainsselin

Mademoiselle Ingrid Thulin's clothes were designed by Marie-Martine

Distribution France: Cocinor; North America: Brandon

Music Giovanni Fusco

EDITOR'S NOTE: Aside from such details as the substitution of Citroëns for Pugeots, there are few discrepancies between script and film. Most of the major ones occur in pages 99–104 where Monsieur Resnais considerably altered the sequence as written by Jorge Semprun and as published here.